The Source® for

by Judy Rudebusch

Content Area	Ages
■ Professional Resource	■ 5-18

	Grades
	■ K-12

Evidence-Based Practice

According to the American Speech-Language-Hearing Association (ASHA) Technical Assistance Paper, Responsiveness to Intervention: New Roles for Speech-Language Pathologists (2006, www.asha.org/members/slp/schools/prof-consult/NewRolesSLP.htm), the National Association of State Directors of Special Education (NASDSE) Response to Intervention: Policy Considerations and Implementation (2005), and the National Research Center on Learning Disabilities (NRCLD) Core Concepts of RTI (2005, www.nrcld.org/research/rti/concepts.shtml), the following response to intervention principles are supported:

- We can effectively teach all children.
- Intervene early.
- Use a multi-tier model of service delivery.
- Use a problem-solving method to make decisions.
- Use research-based, scientifically validated instruction and intervention.
- Monitor student progress to shape instruction.
- Make decisions by using student performance data.
- Use assessment for a variety of purposes.

The information, models, and interventions in this book incorporate these principles and are based on expert professional practice.

LinguiSystems®

LinguiSystems, Inc.
3100 4th Avenue
East Moline, IL 61244
800-776-4332

FAX: 800-577-4555
E-mail: service@linguisystems.com
Web: linguisystems.com

Printed in the U.S.A.

ISBN 978-0-7606-0803-6

About the Author

 **Judy Rudebusch**, M.A., Ed.D., CCC-SLP, holds a doctorate in education administration and has a keen interest in the application of systems theory and best practices for continuous improvement. For over two decades, Judy has applied continuous improvement models to school-based speech-language pathology. She has served as a campus SLP, a program specialist for speech and language services, a special education director, and is currently the division director for special services in a school district in North Texas. Judy participates in national and state initiatives to improve services in schools and is a frequent presenter at workshops and conferences in Texas and across the country.

The Source for RTI is Judy's second publication with LinguiSystems. She is also the author of *LinguiSystems Guide to RTI*.

Dedication

To Marie Morris – mentor, colleague, friend. Your reliance on common sense to solve problems is refreshing. Your passion for excellence in education is contagious.

Table of Contents

Introduction

Response to intervention is a well-integrated system that connects general, compensatory, gifted, and special education in providing high-quality standards-based instruction and intervention. This instruction and intervention is matched to students' academic, social-emotional, and behavioral needs.

The SLP and RTI

The speech-language pathologist (SLP) can play a number of important roles in an RTI framework:

- Team member
- Technical assistance provider
- Curriculum and instruction advisor
- Problem solver
- Direct service provider for assessment and intervention activities

The Source for RTI provides information for the SLP:

- To become familiar with the essential components of effective RTI models
- To design SLP services that are easy to integrate into a multi-tier model of school support

Overview of Content

The standards-based reform and accountability movements are changing conditions in America's schools. Chapter 1 describes the context for change within which RTI evolved, including the Individuals with Disabilities Education Act (IDEA), No Child Left Behind (NCLB) legislation, and the over-identification of children with learning disabilities (LD).

There are eight core principles outlined in chapter 2 that guide and define the structure of an RTI framework. Effective instruction, just-in-time intervention when students fall behind in the grade-level curriculum, and data-driven decisions using student performance data are at the heart of the RTI framework.

RTI models have two or more tiers of increasingly intense, scientific, research-based intervention. Intensity increases from tier to tier through changes in duration, frequency, and time of intervention; group size; and instructor skill level to meet the needs of all students. A three-tier model of school support is described in chapter 3. Pivot points for change, types of speech and language activities for a three-tier model, and tools to facilitate change to RTI are included.

RTI instruction and intervention are based largely on student performance data. Formative assessments (e.g., universal screening and curriculum-based measures) provide ongoing monitoring of students' progress through the curriculum. Chapter 4 provides basic information on curriculum-based measures and use of percentiles for determining which students need additional support and intervention.

Analysis of data for the purposes of improving instruction, aligning curriculum to state standards, and making informed decisions about intervention for individual students is an essential component of the RTI framework. Chapter 5 describes a team problem-solving model for RTI decisions as well as a variety of ways SLPs can participate meaningfully in the RTI problem-solving process.

RTI models include the capacity for substantive changes to traditional methods and procedures that determine eligibility for special education and related services. Chapter 6 presents procedures for SLPs to use RTI data for eligibility recommendations.

There are important roles and responsibilities for SLPs throughout the RTI framework that contribute to the three-prong purpose of RTI–prevention, intervention, and identification. Chapter 7 describes the range of speech and language services, both direct and indirect, that may be considered in an RTI model.

Chapter 8 presents the big picture, describing an integrated RTI framework that serves as a system to connect general, compensatory, gifted, and special education (specifically speech and language services). All students have access to instruction and intervention at all tiers in the three-tier system of school support. Whether a student is in general education or in a special program, each is provided with the essential components of RTI: research- and evidence-based instruction, frequent progress monitoring to measure the student's response to the instruction/intervention, and adjustments to the instruction/intervention if the student does not respond.

A wide variety of sample forms, decision matrices, rubrics, and problem-solving tools are presented in the appendixes to help put the key features of RTI into practice. The Frequently Asked Questions that follow provide a quick reference guide to clarify important aspects of RTI that are explained in more detail elsewhere in this resource.

Frequently Asked Questions

1. **What is the difference between pre-referral intervention and RTI?**

   RTI is more than pre-referral. It is a comprehensive service delivery system that requires significant changes in how a school serves all students. When viewed as a pre-referral system, the intervention remains the province of special education. If RTI is limited to pre-referral activity, the desired integration of general education and special education with the goal of enhanced outcomes for all students will not be achieved.

2. **How does RTI affect referral and evaluation for special education?**

   RTI cannot be used to delay referral for special education evaluation, but in many cases it does provide important information about a student's learning profile. If Tier 2 or Tier 3 intervention does not work to help the student keep pace with grade-level academic and behavior expectations, referral for comprehensive individual evaluation is certainly warranted. Information about the student's responsiveness to intervention is a helpful addition to the information gathered during special education evaluation.

3. **Are all students in Tier 3 intervention enrolled in special education?**

   No. Some multi-tier intervention models described in the literature include special education as the most intensive tier of intervention, so it is possible to define a system in which the specially designed instruction offered through special education is the most intensive intervention provided in the district. The most common approach, however, and the one described in this resource, is to provide assistance and support for students in Tier 2 and Tier 3 prior to referral for special education.

In this three-tier system, all of the tiers of instruction and intervention are available to all students. Students who struggle with grade-level academic and behavior expectations receive focused intervention in Tier 2 or Tier 3 with the goal of closing the performance gap so the student can make progress in the general education classroom without additional support.

4. **What is the research base for RTI?**

Three prongs of research support RTI:

- A three-tier model of school support–both academic and behavioral–has been used to describe an integrated system with efficient resource allocation (Adelman & Taylor 1998; Walker et al. 1996; Vaughn Gross Center for Preventing Reading Difficulties 2005; McCook 2006).
- Problem-solving teams (Hord 2004; Boyd 1992; Nunn & McMahan 2000)
- Curriculum-based assessment procedures (Deno & Mirkin 1977; Deno 1985; Shinn 1989; Nelson 1994).

5. **How long should a student receive Tier 2 or Tier 3 intervention before referral to special education?**

Intervention through the RTI framework cannot delay referral for special education evaluation when there is an obvious disability affecting the student's educational performance. However, Tier 2 or Tier 3 intervention should be provided without referral for special education evaluation as long as the student makes the expected amount of progress at the expected rate. Frequent progress monitoring is a critical component of both Tier 2 and Tier 3 intervention. When this progress monitoring shows the student is making progress and closing the gap between his own performance and the grade-level expectations on the target skill, RTI is working. When the intervention does not work (the gap stays the same or gets wider), a referral to special education is warranted. Length of time in the intervention before referral to special education is individually determined.

6. **Do SLPs have a role in RTI? If SLPs are funded by special education, aren't they limited to working exclusively with students with IEPs?**

Yes. The SLP can play a number of important roles in an RTI framework, including team member, technical assistance provider, curriculum and instruction advisor, problem-solver, and direct service provider for assessment and intervention activities. ASHA (2006) outlined ways that school-based SLPs are uniquely qualified to contribute to RTI efforts in the areas of program design, collaboration, and direct services to individual students.

The wording in IDEA 2004, regarding Early Intervening Services along with the definition of speech-language pathology services in federal regulations, indicate that there is flexibility to go beyond special education when designing speech-language services in the schools.

7. **Is there any difference between Early Intervening Services and RTI?**
Yes. Early Intervening Services (EIS) allow a school district to use up to 15 percent of IDEA 2004 funding to provide services to support students in the classroom in order to prevent placement in special education. Districts use the RTI framework to provide just-in-time intervention for students who are struggling with grade-level academic and behavior expectations in order to prevent more serious problems later. Prevention of placement in special education is a common purpose for both EIS and RTI. EIS describes a funding scheme and RTI describes an intervention model.

8. **How can you use an RTI approach to evaluate learning disabilities?**
Fuchs (2003) proposed a dual discrepancy approach to help determine whether a student has a learning disability in an RTI model. The dual discrepancy consists of below expected level of performance and slower than expected rate of learning even after a period of high-quality instruction in the general education classroom and focused intervention matched to the student's needs. When a significant gap in performance and a slower than expected rate of learning are noted, the student exhibits a learning disability and may need support through special education and related services to help make progress in the general curriculum.

9. **Is RTI just for students with learning disabilities?**
No. RTI approaches are used most frequently to document and monitor effective, engaging instruction in the general education classroom, and to provide just-in-time intervention for any student who struggles to keep pace with grade-level expectations. Response to increasingly intensive intervention is documented and analyzed to insure students' needs are met. All of these activities occur in general education prior to referral for special education evaluation.

10. **Can we implement RTI without doing the problem-solving component?**
    No. The most effective approach to systemic change using an RTI model includes both a multi-tiered system for instruction/intervention and a team problem-solving process. A problem-solving approach is used to examine whether the instruction and intervention are matched to student needs and to monitor the effectiveness of classroom instruction as well as the fidelity and efficacy of focused intervention.

11. **What will SLP services look like in an RTI framework?**
    RTI provides the opportunity for SLPs to participate in early intervention to prevent more serious problems later on. RTI also provides an alternative to using a discrepancy model to assess underachievement. Students who do not respond to high-quality instruction may have a disability. Students who do not respond to additional support for correcting speech and language deficits may have a communication disorder/disability.

    RTI requires nontraditional approaches to assessment, instructional support, and intervention. The RTI framework supports a shift from traditional standardized models of assessment to more pragmatic, educationally relevant models that focus on measuring changes in student performance over time. SLP assessments will include more instructionally relevant and contextually based procedures. SLPs will also have expanded roles with instructional support and intervention that incorporate prevention and identification of students at-risk. Using a "workload approach" to reallocate time will allow the SLP to better address prevention and early intervention activities found in the RTI framework.

12. **Do parents need to be informed about Tier 2 or Tier 3 intervention?**
    Yes. The requirements in IDEA 2004 for parental notice and consent are specifically related to referral, evaluation, and placement in special education/IEP services. However, the RTI framework provides an opportunity to communicate with parents early and seek their involvement and participation in their child's learning with the hopes of preventing more serious learning difficulties. Effective RTI models include procedures to notify and seek parent involvement when student difficulties are first noted, and further to provide written information to parents on a regular basis about their child's progress or lack of it.

13. **How can I use RTI data to help identify a language disorder?**

    Data about a student's responsiveness to intervention is important information to incorporate into evaluation decisions. Look at the student's responsiveness to Tier 2 or Tier 3 language intervention. If the student responds to the intervention, there may not be a language disorder. If the student does not respond as expected, there may be sufficient information to document a language disorder as well as an adverse effect on educational performance resulting from the language disorder.

14. **How can I use RTI to improve speech and language service delivery?**

    Incorporate the following core principles of RTI into your SLP service delivery using a workload approach (ASHA 2002, 2003):

    - Increase your indirect services and activities. Provide information for parents and teachers to support students with speech and language development. Also provide information on the language basis of literacy and learning.

    - Provide Tier 2 and Tier 3 intervention to support students' development of targeted articulation and language skills to prevent more serious problems and to reduce referrals for speech and language (special education) evaluation.

    - Let the "teach-then-test" principle guide your assessments. The RTI framework allows for more pragmatic, educationally relevant models of assessment and intervention that focus on measuring changes in student performance over time.

    - Use scientifically-based research or evidence-based practice (EBP) to guide decisions about your services. EBP allows you to deliver services that are effective in terms of student mastery of communication IEP goals and efficient in terms of how long it takes a student to meet the intervention goals.

    - Use the practice of frequent progress monitoring to determine if your intervention or therapy with students is effective. If a student does not make the expected progress, change your intervention approach.

15. **Is there a difference between scientifically-based research and evidence-based practice?**

    Yes. NCLB and IDEA 2004 require the use of scientifically-based educational practices, defined as "research that involves the application of rigorous, systematic, and objective procedures to obtain reliable and valid knowledge relevant to education activities and programs" (NCLB, 20 U.S.C. Sec. 9101[37]). **Evidence-based practice** (EBP) is a framework for clinical decision-making that integrates good research evidence with clinical expertise and client values. SLPs use this term to describe the reliance on data to make decisions about intervention.

16. **How can I use EBP to make clinical practice decisions?**

    ASHA (2005) issued an official policy document stating that SLPs should integrate EBP principles into clinical decision-making. ASHA recommends considering four factors when making EBP decisions:

    - Evidence from the available clinical research
    - Clinical experience and expertise
    - Information about the client and client values
    - Information about the situation

Response to Intervention is a relatively new approach for schools to help students who struggle to meet grade-level expectations. RTI has deep roots in research in the areas of effective intervention, especially in early reading skills and curriculum-based measures. I sincerely hope you will find *The Source for RTI* an informative, comprehensive, and practical resource that guides your participation in RTI.

Judy

Context for Change

The standards-based reform and accountability for student performance movements are changing conditions in America's schools. Since the mid-1990s, both movements have gained momentum. Perceptions about problems with general and special education systems and over-identification of students with learning disabilities (LD) added to this momentum and led to significant statutory and policy changes.

Standards-Based Reform

Early attempts at reform focused on school management issues, such as compliance with regulations and funding allocations. A 1995 report by the National Education Association (NEA), however, found that states were beginning to shift their focus toward student outcomes. States began adopting standards and tests to assess student performance with the expectation that all children could achieve a certain performance level. This trend in education reform has become known as **standards-based accountability**.

In 1994, Congress passed the Improving America's Schools Act and the Goals 2000: Educate America Act. Both of these laws were aimed at improving the education of all students by

- adopting challenging academic content and performance standards;
- administering assessments aligned with the standards.

Standards identify what students should know and be able to do as they progress in school. Standards are meant to be anchors, aligning curriculum, instruction, and assessment. Each state defines curriculum standards across the content areas for each grade level and then measures student performance according to these standards.

Accountability in Public Education

The federal emphasis on standards continued in 2001 with congressional approval of the No Child Left Behind law (NCLB). The goal of this law is to improve education through a performance-based accountability system built largely around student test results. The emphasis on accountability for performance in NCLB represents an important change. Prior to NCLB, federal initiatives focused on monitoring the provision of services but not on monitoring the quality or effectiveness of the services.

In addition to accountability standards, both NCLB and the Individuals with Disabilities Education Act (IDEA 2004) require the use of research-based, scientifically validated curriculum, instruction, and intervention to the extent available. The purpose of this requirement is to make sure that all students are exposed to curriculum and instruction that has been proven effective for the type of student and the setting.

Attention to student performance data has highlighted wide disparities between groups within the American education system. Students from poverty, urban environments, and racially diverse families typically do not perform as well on state assessments as other students in the same grade.

> **The Reading First initiative increased the federal investment in scientifically-based reading instruction programs in the early grades. The result of this investment is fewer children identified for special education services.**

Accountability standards are applied to all schools and districts that accept Title I funds (which are intended to supplement educational programs for students from low-income families). NCLB requires Title I schools and districts to show Adequate Yearly Progress (AYP) for each subgroup of students based on their race, ethnicity, family income, or special educational needs. The goal of NCLB is that 100 percent of students will score at the proficient level on the state tests in reading and math by the year 2014. Failure to meet AYP for one or more subgroups triggers increasing levels of sanctions, ending with a complete school restructuring after five consecutive years of shortfalls.

Rising Number of Students with Learning Disabilities

There has been a growing concern that too many children were identified as learning disabled (LD) under IDEA. In the 1990s alone, the number of students aged 6–21 identified as having LD increased 38 percent. Six percent of all students in schools are identified with LD, which is greater than 50 percent of the special education population. Eighty to 90 percent of children with LD are impaired in reading (USDE 2003). The Special Education Commission (2002) reported that two out of five children are in special education because they cannot read adequately.

Prior to the re-authorization of IDEA 2004, eligibility determination for LD was based on finding a significant discrepancy between ability (as measured on intelligence tests) and achievement (as measured on academic achievement tests). School psychologists, speech-language pathologists, and other assessment specialists focused on a test-and-treat model, which emphasized documenting a discrepancy through the referral and eligibility process. Educators placed little emphasis on prevention and early identification of learning problems. In addition, they did little to measure effectiveness of the specially designed instruction once students were placed in special education.

Both researchers and policy makers are concerned about the overemphasis on confirming a learning disability and a lack of consistency in classification. Although all states serve students with LD, studies show differences across states in prevalence, characteristics of students, classification criteria, and special education programs. For example, the prevalence of students with LD varies from 2.8 percent in Kentucky to 9.4 percent in Rhode Island (Reschly & Hosp 2004). Peterson and Shinn (2002) found wide variation in the characteristics and prevalence of students with LD across districts within the same state.

The message is that school districts often identify students as having LD when, in fact, these students have not been adequately taught. The problem does not lie within the student but rests within the educational delivery system. Lyon and Fletcher (2001) proposed that the rise in the incidence of LD is largely the result of three factors:

- Remediation is rarely effective after 2nd grade.
- Referral and assessment procedures work against identifying children with LD before 2nd grade.
- Federal policy and the weight of compliance and the status quo allow ineffective policies to continue unchecked.

Concerns about increasing numbers of students with disabilities needing special education lead to focused examination of the benefits of special education for student achievement.

Remediation through Special Education

Several research studies showed little benefit from special education in terms of closing the achievement gap for students with disabilities. In an analysis of a large data set, Hanushek, Kain, and Rivkin (2002) found very small gains from special education for students with LD in grades 3–6 for both reading and math. They concluded that special education did not show good results because the quality of instruction was poor (too general and unsystematic) and was provided too late (many children lose their motivation to learn to read after a year or more of failure). In another study of children with severe reading disabilities in grades 3–5, Torgeson (2000) found very little change in students' word reading and reading comprehension after 16 months in special education.

The emphasis on testing and placement (rather than on instruction matched to students' needs) and the resulting poor outcomes for students placed in special education has impacted education policy.

Research and Policy Considerations

Several consensus reports on reading and on special education were published following authorization of NCLB (2001) and in preparation for re-authorization of IDEA (2004). These reports substantiated a need for change in literacy instruction and in the way we identify LD. They also suggested that RTI models may break the cycle of over-identification of language and learning disabilities in children. Each of these reports contributed to the adoption of RTI.

▶ **National Reading Panel (NRP 2000)**
The National Reading Panel identified the essential components of early reading instruction supported in the literature, including phonemic awareness, phonics, vocabulary, reading fluency, and reading comprehension. Overt reading instruction using a balanced literacy approach is an important issue in special education since most students identified with LD have reading problems.

▶ **President's Commission on Excellence in Special Education (2001)**
President George W. Bush established this Commission to make recommendations for priorities and improvement of IDEA. The Commission gathered information from hearings and the testimonies of researchers, teachers, parents, and observers. The majority of the recommendations are consistent with RTI practices:

- Focus on results—not on a process.
- Focus on a model of prevention—not a model of failure.
- Consider children with disabilities as general education children first.

▶ **National Summit on Learning Disabilities (Bradley, Danielson, & Hallahan 2002)**

This summit was sponsored by the Office of Special Education Programs in the U.S. Department of Education to consider alternatives to identification of LD. The researchers concluded that the traditional method for LD identification was not grounded in scientific research. They supported "response to quality intervention" as the most promising method of identification. The researchers pointed out that this approach could promote effective practices in schools.

▶ **National Research Council Panel on Minority Representation (Donovan & Cross 2002)**

The National Research Council Panel pointed out the absence of research confirming the benefits of special education programs for minority students. This report focused on prevention and early intervention to reduce the risk conditions that result in over-identification of poor and minority students in special education. The Panel described a four-tier system of intervention and treatment with alternative approaches to disability identification. It made the following recommendations for determining LD eligibility:

- Large difference compared to peers in academic or behavioral performance
- Low response rate to high-quality intervention
- Struggle with grade-level material results in poor performance in the general education classroom
- Need for specially designed instruction through special education
- Exclusion of other causes, including sensory impairments, other disabilities, and no opportunity to learn

Speech and Language Services in Schools

Speech-language pathologists (SLPs) experience many of the same challenges identified in the research as limitations in special education:

- Inconsistent eligibility determination from district to district and state to state
- Emphasis on eligibility and placement rather than on effective intervention

- Reliance on assessment practices that use discrepancy models to identify speech and language disorders
- Difficulty coordinating services with general education teachers
- Difficulty integrating services with grade-level curriculum standards
- Little scientifically-based research to guide selection of intervention methodology; little outcome data to guide practice
- Restrictions on use of time, with little time left to focus on prevention of communication disorders

Recent advances in speech-language pathology appear promising for increasing the quality of service in schools through coordinated services and early intervention. Information about using a workload approach for caseload management (ASHA 2002), evidence-based practice (ASHA 2006), and implementing IDEA 2004 for educationally relevant services (ASHA 2007) provide a platform for the SLP to contribute to better outcomes for students.

The SLP's Roles in Supporting Change

The school-based SLP is in a position to participate in school improvement efforts. RTI models provide a framework to support better outcomes in schools and SLPs play a number of important roles in an RTI framework:

- Team member
- Technical assistance provider
- Curriculum and instruction advisor
- Problem-solver
- Direct service provider for assessment and intervention activities

ASHA (2006) outlined ways that school-based SLPs are uniquely qualified to contribute to RTI efforts. (These activities will be described in more detail in chapter 7.)

▶ **Program Design**
- Explain the role that language plays in curriculum, assessment, and instruction.
- Explain the interconnection between spoken and written language.
- Identify existing literature on scientifically-based literacy assessment and intervention approaches.

- Assist in the selection of screening measures.
- Help identify systemic patterns of student need with respect to language skills.
- Provide professional development on the language basis of literacy and learning.

▶ **Collaboration**

- Assist classroom teachers with screening.
- Participate in the development of progress-monitoring systems and analysis of student outcomes.
- Participate on problem-solving teams.
- Collaborate with other specialists to implement RTI.
- Interpret screening results and progress-monitoring information for families.

▶ **Serving Individual Students**

- Conduct expanded speech sound error screening and oral language screening for K-3 students to track students at-risk.
- Intervene with students who are highly stimulable as prevention of more serious problems later.
- Help decide when to refer for a speech and language evaluation.
- Use norm-referenced, standardized, and informal assessments to determine whether students have speech and language disorders.
- Determine duration, intensity, frequency, and type of service that students with communication disorders may need.
- Collaborate with classroom teachers to provide services and support for students with communication disabilities.
- Identify, use, and disseminate evidence-based practices for speech and language services or RTI intervention.

Core Principles of RTI

The Response to Intervention (RTI) framework includes eight core principles that guide and define its structure. Attention to all of the core principles is essential for developing strong infrastructure to provide effective instruction for every student.

- We can effectively teach all children.
- Intervene early.
- Use a multi-tier model of service delivery.
- Use a problem-solving method to make decisions.
- Use research-based, scientifically validated instruction and intervention.
- Monitor student progress to shape instruction.
- Make decisions by using student performance data.
- Use assessment for a variety of purposes.

▶ **We can effectively teach all children.**

No Child Left Behind (2001) heightened the need for delivery of consistent, high-quality instruction in all classrooms. Teachers need the knowledge, skills, curriculum, tools, and materials to provide explicit and systematic instruction.

Explicit and systematic instruction does not leave anything to chance. For example, explicit instruction in early reading requires teachers to make direct connections between the letters in print and the sounds in words, and it requires teaching of these relationships in a comprehensive fashion. It also requires direct teaching and explicit practice of word meanings. Finally, explicit and systematic instruction in early reading requires not only direct practice to build fluency, but also careful, sequential instruction and practice using comprehension strategies to construct meaning. Most importantly, explicit and systematic instruction is needed in every classroom, not only for reading, but for every subject area to ensure effective teaching for all children.

Consistent, high-quality instruction rests on the platform of a model of teaching such as the one provided by Frey and Fisher (2006). The Gradual

Release of Responsibility Model is a widely-used model of instruction. It is based on the work of Vygotsky (1978) and Pearson and Fielding (1991). The instructional sequence gradually moves each student from teacher-dependence to learning-independence (See figure 1 below). The teacher focuses the lesson with explicit instruction, uses guided instruction and student teamwork to practice the skills, and finally, allows students to demonstrate independent mastery of the skill. Teacher versus student responsibility is on a continuum. The teacher has a great deal of responsibility during explicit instruction, shared responsibility during guided instruction, and less responsibility as students demonstrate independence with the skill. At the same time, students start out with less responsibility and take on more responsibility as they internalize learning and become independent in demonstrating the skill.

Figure 1
A Model of Instruction that Works

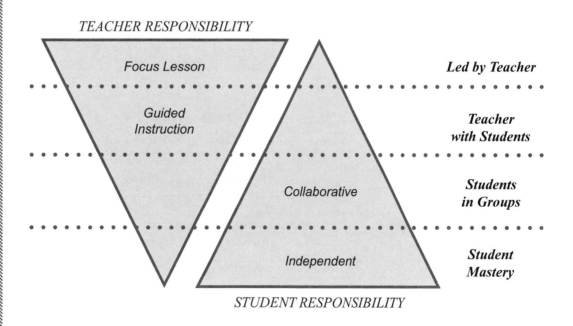

▶ **Intervene early.**

The goal of early intervention is to provide the necessary support as soon as a student shows signs of academic or behavioral struggle in order to increase the student's developmental and educational gains and to keep the student on pace with others in the same grade. There is evidence–both quantitative and qualitative–that early intervention results in children needing fewer special education and other rehabilitative services later in life and that children are retained in grade less often. Longitudinal data on disadvantaged children who participated in a preschool project showed that they had maintained significant gains at age 19, and they were more committed to schooling and employment than disadvantaged children who did not attend preschool (Berrueta-Clement, Schweinhart, Barnett, Epstein, & Weikart 1984).

According to the U.S. Department of Education, there are three primary reasons to intervene during the preschool years:

- Enhance the child's development
- Provide support and assistance to the family
- Maximize the child's and family's benefit to society

IDEA 2004 supports the RTI concept of early intervention to prevent school failure.

> A local education agency may use up to 15 percent of its federal funding… "to develop and implement coordinated, early intervening services…for students in kindergarten through grade 12 (with a particular emphasis on students in kindergarten through grade 3) who have not been identified as needing special education or related services but who need additional academic and behavioral support to succeed in a general education environment." [P.L. 108-46, §613(f)(1)]

▶ **Use a multi-tier model of service delivery.**

A multi-tier model of service delivery has two goals:

- Prevent future academic problems by providing just-in-time intervention for students who struggle to meet academic and behavioral expectations.
- Assist in identifying students with specific learning disabilities (LD).

In this service delivery model, all students receive quality academic instruction and behavior support from highly qualified, well-trained teachers. Quality classroom instruction should fully meet the needs of 80-90 percent of students. RTI works well when all classroom instruction is research-based and incorporates measurement of students' progress in the grade-level curriculum. Measurement activities may include ongoing universal screening of all students in the grade level, periodic progress monitoring, and prescriptive assessment.

Students identified in their classroom as at-risk, performing below expected levels, or requiring specific supports to make adequate progress should receive focused intervention to address the problem. Multi-tier models allow for increasing levels of support for struggling students by providing intervention aimed at preventing more serious problems in the future or remediating the skill or behavior causing the problems in the classroom. Intervention can vary from small groups using structured programs and activities to intensive, individualized intervention that is provided more often and for longer periods of time.

Students who need additional support continue to receive quality instruction in the classroom in addition to intervention to meet individual needs. The combined approach of quality classroom instruction and intervention should meet the requirements of these 10 to 20 percent of students. Information about students' response to intervention can then help identify students with specific learning disabilities (LD).

▶ **Use a problem-solving method to make decisions within a multi-tier model.**
Problem solving to meet individual student needs is an essential feature of the RTI framework. Research supports the effectiveness of using a clearly defined method to determine student need and to develop and evaluate responsiveness to intervention (Fuchs, Fuchs, & Compton 2005; Vaughn & Wanzek 2006; Haagaer, Klingner, & Vaughn 2007).

There are several problem-solving models described in the literature. Most of these models describe some variation of the Plan–Do–Study–Act (PDSA) cycle popularized by Deming during the 1940s in his work on continuous improvement and system change (Walton 1986). In the RTI framework, an effective problem-solving process uses the skills of professionals from different disciplines to develop and evaluate instruction and intervention to improve school performance for all students. The problem-solving process should have mechanisms for

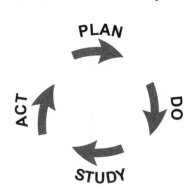

- defining the problem in measurable terms;
- analyzing the problem and variables that contribute to the problem;
- developing a plan to address the problem;
- implementing the plan;
- evaluating the plan's effectiveness.

▶ **Use research-based, scientifically validated instruction and intervention.**

Selection and implementation of scientifically-based instruction/intervention increases the probability of positive individual responsiveness to intervention for students who are not keeping pace with other students in the same grade. Scientifically-based research is defined as follows:

> "…research that involves the application of rigorous, systematic, and objective procedures to obtain reliable and valid knowledge relevant to education activities and programs." (NCLB, 20 U.S.C. §9101 [37])

SLPs use the term **evidence-based practice** (EBP) to describe this same reliance on data to make decisions about intervention (Moore-Brown & Montgomery 2001). SLPs must base their daily instructional methods and intervention on good evidence and not on what has "always been done" or what materials are available. Evidence-based practice allows an SLP to select treatments that are clinically acceptable based on good research evidence, consistent with the SLP's clinical expertise, and in keeping with client values (ASHA 2005). It is becoming increasingly important for SLPs to articulate the evidence, or research-basis, for their delivery of services.

The IDEA 2004 Congressional Statement of Findings includes key considerations that strengthen reauthorization of this law, including the following cautionary statement about special education outcomes:

> "…the implementation of [IDEA] has been impeded by low expectations and an insufficient focus on applying replicable research on proven methods of teaching and learning for children with disabilities." (IDEA 2004 §601[c]).

Clearly, there is an expectation for us to use empirical data about instruction and intervention—to use approaches that we know work with children. Emphasis on EBP in school-based speech-language pathology helps us become better clinicians and better action-researchers. Attention to EBP helps us be accountable for increasing student performance and also reminds us to keep effectiveness data about how well our intervention works with students.

▶ **Monitor student progress to shape instruction.**
The only way to determine if intervention is working is to monitor student progress and to use the information to shape ongoing instruction and intervention. Determining the effectiveness (or lack of effectiveness) of an intervention is important to maximize the impact of focused intervention for struggling students. When an intervention does not work with a student, stop or change the intervention to meet the student's needs in a timely way.

▶ **Make decisions by using student performance data.**
Decisions within the RTI problem-solving model are based on professional judgment using student performance data and consideration of research-based, scientifically validated evidence and information about a student. This core principle of the RTI framework requires systems and processes within the school district that allow for

- ongoing data collection;
- capacity to analyze the data and generate useful information from the data;
- expectation that this data will be used to make informed instructional decisions at every level of the RTI framework.

▶ **Use assessment for a variety of purposes.**

- Screen all children to identify those who are not making academic or behavioral progress at expected rates.
- Periodically monitor all students' progress in the curriculum.
- Frequently monitor target skill/s and responsiveness to the intervention.
- Complete more comprehensive group or individual curriculum-based assessments.

Effective instruction for every student and effective, early support for students who struggle to meet grade-level expectations are central themes in RTI. Each of the core principles of RTI is examined in more detail in subsequent chapters to help school-based speech-language pathologists contribute to continuous school improvement and success for every student.

RTI and the Three-Tier Model of School Support

The educational system in the United States is not meeting the needs of all students. Current estimates of the number of students who are at risk for school failure range from 20 to 30 percent of the total school population. These estimates are clearly not acceptable and provide the impetus for change.

Multi-Tier Models of School Support

Multi-tier models of school support provide the framework needed to match instruction and intervention to student needs and to track how well students respond to changes in instruction. For sake of illustration, a three-tier model is described in this chapter. The practices described in the three-tier model would be included in any multi-tier model; the components would simply be grouped differently.

The three-tier system provides increasing intensity of instruction to students in direct proportion to individual needs. Each tier has a set of support structures or activities that helps teachers implement research-based curriculum and instructional practices designed to improve student achievement.

The Three-Tier Model of School Support (NASDSE 2006) is designed to meet the needs of all students. (See appendix A on page 106.) The Three-Tier RTI Model on the right is adapted from the NASDSE model. The instruction and intervention involved in each of the tiers is explained in more detail in chapters 4 and 5.

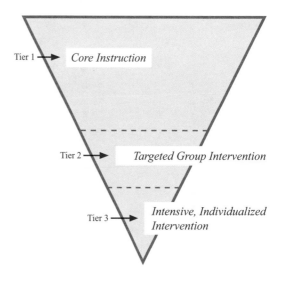

Tier 1 Core Instruction

Tier 1 Core Instruction includes the following elements:

- Scientifically-based curriculum following state standards
- Behavioral support systems
- Effective, highly engaging instruction
- Well-trained teachers
- Universal screening and periodic monitoring

▶ **Scientifically-based Curriculum Following State Standards**
School districts establish a core instructional program by choosing curricula that align with state standards. It is also important that curricula have evidence of producing adequate levels of achievement for the majority of students. If most of the students are meeting benchmarks for their grade level and time of year, then it may be presumed that the foundation program is sufficient and effective.

▶ **Behavioral Support Systems**
Behavioral supports are provided in the following ways:

- Direct, explicit instruction for learning behavior that is matched to students' age and developmental level
- Classroom and school-wide routines and procedures that facilitate the expected learning behaviors
- Opportunities to practice learning behaviors
- Clearly stated expectations
- Adjustments to curriculum and instructional delivery as a first response to behavior problems
- Dynamic, differentiated, high-interest instruction
- Structured opportunities for students to learn from their mistakes in a positive rather than punitive manner

▶ **Effective, Highly Engaging Instruction**
Schools and school systems can provide the infrastructure for effective, highly engaging instruction that meets all students' needs. Effective teaching stems from understanding how students learn, understanding

which instructional strategies work well, and knowing how to organize instruction to provide students with the substance of what they need to learn. Dynamic and interesting instruction that engages each student's mind and attention is critical for student success across Tiers 1, 2, and 3. Teachers should consider the following three dimensions in their instruction (Pearson & Fielding 1991):

- Task control—decisions about the task, how to involve students in the task, and how to assess that involvement
- Authenticity—how meaningful and relevant the learning is to the students' lives
- Teacher's role—when, where, and to what extent the teacher will participate in each task

▶ **Well-trained Teachers**

Quality, relevant staff development is one of the keys to high student achievement (Roy & Hord 2003; Hord 2004). Answers to the following questions can help guide effective staff development:

- What do our students need to know and do that they currently don't know and aren't able to do?
- What do teachers need to know and do in order to help our students?

As the quality of teacher training improves, the number of students at risk for failure will decrease and the share of resources available to provide Tier 2 and Tier 3 intervention will be sufficient.

▶ **Universal Screening and Periodic Monitoring**

All students are screened in essential academic areas. Students' progress is monitored at the beginning, middle, and end of the year. Results from the screenings and assessments provide the following important information:

- Whether students are making adequate progress
- Which students need assistance so they do not fall further behind
- When to modify instruction to ensure that students master essential skills

In some situations, and in addition to screening and periodic monitoring of student progress, a group-level diagnostic assessment is given to students who struggle with Core Instruction. These assessment results help determine what students can and cannot do in specific academic and behavioral domains. This information is then used to adjust the delivery of the curriculum and instruction and/or plan for Tier 2 Targeted Group Intervention.

Tier 2 Targeted Group Intervention

Up to 20 percent of students may be identified in Tier 1 as having the following characteristics:

- At-risk
- Performing below expected levels
- Requiring specific supports to make grade-level progress in Tier 1

These students receive Targeted Group Intervention as well as Core Instruction. Tier 2 intervention is provided in small, same-ability groups of up to four students. Intervention at this level should provide sufficient additional support for these students to gain the skills and strategies needed to close the achievement gap and continue to make grade-level progress in Tier 1 Core Instruction (only).

Tier 2 Targeted Group Intervention includes the following elements:

- Evidence-based practice protocols
- Behavioral support and intervention
- Effective, highly engaging instruction
- Skilled teachers/service providers
- Frequent progress monitoring

▶ **Evidence-based Practice Protocols**

Tier 2 intervention is specialized, systematic, purposeful, focused, and consistent. It is often scripted or very structured. Evidence-based practices in the form of standard treatments are provided for students with similar needs. Tier 2 intervention has a high probability of producing change for a large number of students who need support for mastering a target skill or behavior.

▶ **Behavioral Support and Intervention**

Tier 2 intervention includes the following focused intervention for students whose behavior interferes with learning:

- Direct, explicit intervention related to the interfering behavior
- Specialized behavior plans that outline the target behavior, timeline for improving behavior, frequency of Tier 2 intervention, and exit criteria for returning to Tier 1 Core Instruction (only)

▶ **Effective, Highly Engaging Instruction**

Tier 2 intervention may use classroom materials and approaches, but it extends and augments Tier 1 instruction in these ways:

- Providing more opportunities for students to process and practice the target skill or behavior
- Breaking the material into smaller chunks or segments

Tier 2 may also provide different instructional methods and pacing of instruction, making overt connections between what the students currently know and what they need to learn. This intervention must be of high interest and high value to the students in order to provide meaningful support and limit the time needed at this level.

▶ **Skilled Teachers/Service Providers**

Tier 2 intervention is provided by specially trained classroom teachers or specialists such as speech-language pathologists, reading specialists, or behavior specialists. Professional development for Tier 2 teachers and other services providers is focused, specialized, and ongoing. Student responsiveness to the Tier 2 intervention is used to make decisions about the need for additional professional training.

▶ **Frequent Progress Monitoring**

At Tier 2, it is important to frequently monitor students' progress on acquiring the target skill/s or behavior/s—every two to three weeks—and to fine-tune the intervention based on student response. In addition to monitoring students' response to Tier 2 intervention, curriculum-based assessments and functional behavior assessments may be administered.

Students receive Tier 2 intervention as long as needed to bring skills up to grade-level expectations or as long as their response to intervention is positive and sufficient to justify continuing. When a particular student's needs have been met through Tier 2 intervention, the student returns to Tier 1 Core Instruction (only).

Tier 3 Intensive, Individualized Intervention

Students who continue to struggle without measurable progress in Tier 1 and Tier 2 instruction/intervention move to Tier 3 intervention. One to five percent of students who have received Tier 2 intervention continue to have significant difficulty acquiring the necessary skills to make progress in Tier 1 instruction. These students need more frequent, explicit, intensive, individualized intervention for longer periods of time. Intervention at this level may or may not be provided through special education.

Tier 3 Intensive, Individualized Intervention includes the following elements:

- Research-based and evidence-based intervention
- Intensive, individualized intervention
- Increased duration
- Behavioral support and intervention
- Skilled teachers/service providers
- Very frequent progress monitoring

▶ **Research-based and Evidence-based Intervention**

Tier 3 intervention approaches should meet the following criteria:

- Supported by scientifically-based research
- Supported by evidence that the intervention has been effective for other students working on the target skill
- Structured, explicit, and specifically tailored to learning targets

▶ **Intensive, Individualized Intervention**

Tier 3 is the most intensive intervention. It targets specific deficiency areas in order to meet individual student needs. If a student's response to Tier 2 was positive but slower than desired, he or she may continue to receive a similar type of intervention. In this case, however, the frequency may be increased to daily intervention in addition to Tier 1 Core Instruction. For example, a Tier 2 intervention of two 30-minute sessions per week may be increased to at least one hour per day (two 30-minute sessions) when the student moves to Tier 3. At this level, the student receives intervention alone or in very small, same-ability groups (two to three students).

▶ **Increased Duration**

Tier 3 intervention is provided for students over a longer period of time than Tier 2. Daily, intensive, individualized intervention will likely be provided for a minimum of 12 weeks and in some cases continue for up to 18 weeks. Decisions about continuing Tier 3 intervention are made based on student performance and rate of progress in mastering the target skill or behavior.

▶ **Behavioral Support and Intervention**

At Tier 3, students with behavioral needs require specialized behavior plans. These students receive intensive intervention in pull-out sessions to see if this level of support sufficiently minimizes the effects of interfering behavior on learning. Intervention may be provided by or monitored by behavior specialists, school counselors, or licensed specialists in school psychology. Close collaboration with the classroom teacher and parents is essential.

▶ **Skilled Teachers/Service Providers**

As in Tier 2, specially-trained classroom teachers or specialists (e.g., SLPs, reading specialists, behavior specialists) provide Tier 3 intervention. Professional development for Tier 3 teachers and service providers is focused, specialized, and ongoing.

▶ **Very Frequent Progress Monitoring**

At Tier 3, a student's response to intervention is very frequently monitored (one or more times per week). In addition, an individual diagnostic assessment that is skills-based, curriculum-based, and linked directly to grade-level expectations should focus the intervention and progress monitoring of specific skills that the student needs to learn.

A chart summarizing the various parameters of instruction and intervention in the Three-Tier RTI Model of Instruction follows on the next page.

Three-Tier RTI Model of Instruction

	Tier 1 Core Instruction	Tier 2 Targeted Group Intervention	Tier 3 Intensive, Individualized Intervention
Focus	All students	Students who do not respond to Tier 1	Students who are significantly behind and do not respond to Tier 1 or 2
Program	Scientifically-based curricula following state standards	Specialized, research- or evidence-based interventions	Intensive, specialized, research- or evidence-based interventions
Instruction	Engaging, high-quality instruction	Engaging, high quality; may be same materials as classroom; different methods	Engaging, explicit, intensive; different materials, methods, pace; longer duration
Grouping	Multiple and flexible grouping formats	Same-ability small groups of up to 4 students	Individual or very small same-ability groups (2 or 3 students)
Time	As required by state for different content areas	20-40 minutes, 3-5 days per week in addition to Tier 1	45+ minutes daily in addition to Tier 1
Assessment	Universal screening and interim assessment at beginning, middle, and end of year	Progress monitoring every 2-3 weeks on target skill/s to measure student response to intervention	Progress monitoring every week on target skill/s to measure student response to intervention
Behavior Support	Effective behavior supports provided through classroom routines; information provided to parents	Specialized behavior plans implemented/monitored by teacher and parents	Specialized behavior plans and activities provided in pull-out sessions in coordination with teacher and parents
Interventionist	General education classroom teacher	Classroom teacher or specialist (e.g., SLP, reading specialist, or behavior specialist)	Designated by the school; usually a specialist (e.g., SLP, reading specialist, or behavior specialist)
Setting	General education classroom	Pull-out small group or additional intervention in classroom (not by classroom teacher)	Pull-out from classroom to different learning environment
Professional Development	Ongoing to provide teachers with necessary tools to promote engaging delivery of curricula	Focused, specialized, and ongoing to provide training in specialized interventions	Focused, specialized, and ongoing to provide training in specialized interventions
Problem-Solving Team	Reviews screening results and interim assessment data; Assists teacher in decisions about which students need Tier 2	Reviews progress-monitoring data to determine which students are responding (back to Tier 1 with monitoring) or not responding (change Tier 2 intervention or provide Tier 3)	Reviews progress-monitoring data to determine which students are responding (back to Tier 1 with monitoring) or not responding (change Tier 3 intervention or consider additional individual evaluation or referral for special education evaluation)
Parent Involvement	Information about student progress routinely provided to parents via report cards and parent-teacher conferences	Student progress on target skill/s provided to parents every two weeks; parents included in decisions about changing intervention	Ongoing, frequent communication with parents regarding progress on target skill/s; parents included in decisions about changing intervention
Outcome	Fully meets needs of 80-90% of students	With Tier 1 Core Instruction, meets needs of 5-15% of students	With Tier 1 Core Instruction meets needs of 2-5% of students

The Source for RTI
Copyright © 2008 LinguiSystems, Inc.

Pivot Points for Change

RTI requires change in approaches to classroom instruction, instructional support, intervention, assessment, and measurement of each student's progress in mastering grade-level standards. Change occurs along a pathway:

Awareness ⟶ **Interest** ⟶ **Desire** ⟶ **Action**

(Government Office for the South West 2007)

Along this pathway, pressure for change is created when leaders in a district or at a school demonstrate commitment to the change. A clear, shared vision of RTI must be established and the school must allow for change by providing the resources. At the level of "Action," it is important to engage in open communication and reflection about how the model is working in the school and for individual students. This model (adapted from Deming) is an effective way to support communication and reflection about the change process.

As SLPs, we have the opportunity to fully participate in improving education for all students through an RTI framework.

▶ **Open Attitude**

We often assume change means adding more to what we already do. Change actually means that we reconfigure what we do. With an open attitude about changing the way we provide services in schools, we can contribute our expertise to the RTI system and to problem solving for individual students.

▶ **Redirected Effort**

The Three-Tier RTI Model provides instruction and intervention through general education. If you redirect some of your efforts to the **prevention** of communication disorders, you will see the effect of RTI in at least two ways.

Smaller Caseload: Fewer students will be referred for evaluation and IEP services, and therefore, fewer students will be identified for speech and language therapy.

Larger Impact: You will have a positive impact on more students than with traditional service delivery.

▶ **Outcomes Orientation**

SLPs are interested in students' communicative competence as it relates to academic achievement and functional performance in the grade-level curriculum. With an outcomes orientation, we can more easily shift from traditional models of evaluation and service delivery to more pragmatic, educationally relevant models that measure and support student performance over time. As participants in RTI, we can help in the following ways:

- Prevention of learning problems
- Intervention to support students who are struggling
- New ways to identify students with learning disabilities

▶ **Managing Change**

It is important to think about the following as you participate in changing to a Three-Tier RTI Model in your district or school:

- Use a systems approach so that once implemented, RTI can be sustained.
- Be a part of the RTI team at your school.
- Share information with teachers about communicative competence, about how to help their students become proficient communicators, and about language demands in the curriculum.
- Stay grounded in research-based and evidence-based practice.
- Be prepared for the "implementation dip" (Fullan 1993) when things seem to get worse before they get better.
- Make plans, but hold your plans "loosely" (Sparks 1993). Clarity of purpose is important. Flexibility is more powerful than rigidity when working out the details of the RTI plan for change.
- Do only as much as you can. When we take on too much or too many different things, professional paralysis sets in.

Types of Speech and Language Activities for the Three-Tier Model

▶ **Tier 1 SLP Activities**

- Provide information and activities for parents and teachers to support students' speech and language development.

- Encourage oral language development in kindergarten and first grade in socio-dramatic play centers, listening centers, and "Good Speech" centers.

- Provide oral language-rich lessons in second and third grade to promote development of speech and language skills and effective communication behavior.

- Use scripted stories and story grammar with third, fourth, and fifth graders to practice the similarities and differences between oral and written language conventions.

- Provide professional development on the language basis of literacy.

- Find correlations between grade-level standards in the curriculum and communication skills. Provide the information to teachers. (See examples of these correlations across grade levels and subject areas from the Texas standards in appendix B on page 107.)

▶ **Tier 2 SLP Activities**

- Assist in the selection of research-based or evidence-based literacy interventions.

- Provide articulation or language-specific intervention programs to prevent more serious problems later on or to remediate problems when students seem highly stimulable and ready for change.

- Identify, use, and disseminate evidence-based practices for speech and language skills and communication behaviors related to Tier 2 intervention.

- Assist in determining when students need Tier 2 intervention or when referral to special education for speech and language disorders is warranted. (See Three-Tier RTI Decision Matrix, appendix C, page 111.)

- Conduct frequent progress monitoring of target skill/s for students in Tier 2 speech or language intervention (at least every two to three weeks).

▶ **Tier 3 SLP Activities**

- Assist in the selection of research-based literacy interventions.

- Provide articulation or language-specific intervention programs for remediation of problems.

- Work closely with Tier 3 service providers to determine when referral to special education for speech and language disorders/ communication disability is warranted. (See Three-Tier RTI Decision Matrix, appendix C, page 111.) For example, an eighth-grade student who is learning English and who has gaps in schooling may benefit from Tier 3 intervention. This student may not need a referral to special education because he has a language difference, not a suspected language disorder.

- Conduct weekly progress monitoring of target skill/s for students in Tier 3 speech or language intervention.

- Use a Workload Approach for scheduling Three-Tier RTI activities. (More information on this approach is provided in chapter 6 on page 76. See Flexible Schedules and RTI/Evaluation Activities, appendix D, page 112.)

RTI and Data-Driven Decisions

Schools collect considerable information about students but do not always consistently and systematically use this data to make decisions. Consider the wealth of data available about most students:

attendance	recent trauma	socio-economic status
race/gender	special health needs	suspensions/expulsions
medical care	home language	extracurricular activities
grades	promotion/retention	identification of disabilities
mobility/stability	discipline referrals	family demographics

In addition, schools track performance on nationally normed tests, criterion-referenced tests, state normed tests, curriculum-based measurements, and standardized tests, as well as performance in comparison to other students in the nation/state/district/classroom, and NCLB proficiency scores for Adequate Yearly Progress (AYP).

In the RTI approach, educators use all of the information available about a student to understand the factors that contribute to academic or behavioral struggle and to guide decisions about meeting student needs. Educators cannot make informed, consistent decisions about the effectiveness of instruction and intervention without valid data about students' responses to the instruction and intervention.

RTI Assessments

Assessment information is important for making the following decisions:

- Where students are in relation to the curriculum
- Which students need specialized intervention
- When the intervention has worked
- Whether students are making expected progress
- When to make a referral to special education
- Whether instruction and/or intervention are adequate for meeting students' needs

There are three primary types of assessment that provide data for these decisions.

Screening assessments—used to determine which students may have problems

Diagnostic assessments—conducted when more in-depth analysis of a student's strengths and weaknesses is needed to guide instruction

Progress-monitoring assessments—conducted on a routine basis and matched to the curriculum in order to estimate amount and rate of progress and to gauge effectiveness of instruction/intervention

RTI instruction and intervention are based largely on student performance data. Instruction and intervention are designed based on results of screening, diagnostic, and progress-monitoring assessments.

▶ **Screening Assessments**

Screening assessment is the first step in identifying students who may be at risk. The sooner we identify children who need support, the easier it is to help them catch up.

In RTI, the term **universal screening** describes short tests of broad aspects of the curriculum that are critical to success in school. A good screening test has the following features:

- Norm-referenced—either locally-developed norms or a norm sample that matches the group being screened
- Valid—measures what it says it measures
- Reliable—consistently measures the same skills or behaviors
- Sensitive—correctly identifies students who may be at risk
- Specific—correctly excludes students without problems
- Short
- Easy to administer and score
- Easy to interpret

Screening results should show which students are proficient and independent with the skills (above average), which students are in the process of developing the skills (average), and which students are significantly deficient in the skills (below average). Average performance is between the 25th and 75th percentile with the 50th percentile showing where half of the students scored above and half scored below the median. When large numbers of students have poor performance on the screening, non-student variables (e.g., the curriculum scope and sequence or the teacher's knowledge, skills, or instructional delivery) may need to be changed.

> A cut score is the minimum level of performance needed to demonstrate that a task has been performed at a specified standard. The cut score is the breaking line between proficient performance and less than proficient performance. Students who perform below the cut score in a Tier 1 screening or assessment are referred to the RTI problem-solving team.

Teachers can chart students' performance on the universal screening in terms of the band of percentiles for above average, average, and below average. The RTI team then has the information for the class/grade to establish cut scores. They will use the cut scores to identify which students to consider for additional support. (See figure 1 below and figure 2 on page 42.) Figure 1 shows a frequency distribution chart of raw scores on the universal screening for all first graders in the school. In this example, a 20-item screening was administered to 90 first graders. The chart shows the range of scores (from 1 item to 20 items correct) and the pattern of performance (majority of scores were between 5 and 15 items correct).

Figure 1
Universal Screening
Frequency Distribution of Raw Scores for First Grade

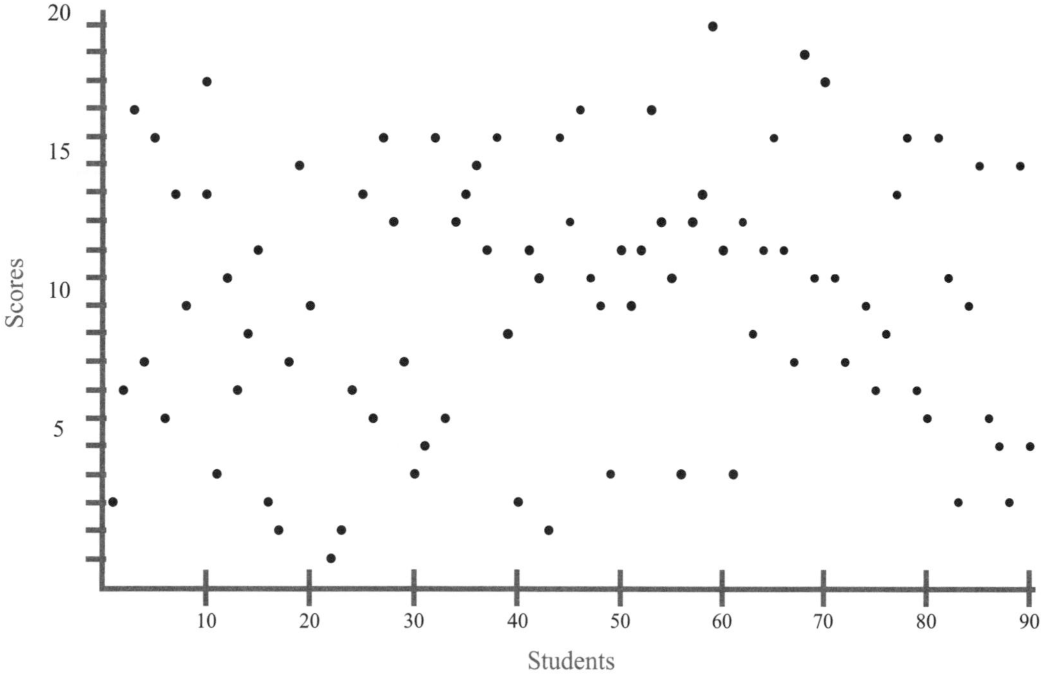

Items Passed	1-5	6-10	11-15	16-20
Frequency Score	18	20	38	14

Figure 2 shows students' scores for one first-grade class. Percentile ranks were calculated based on scores of all first graders. In the class shown in figure 2, 6 students scored at or above the 75th percentile, 11 students scored in the average range between the 25th and 75th percentiles, and 5 students scored below the cut score (25th percentile). These 5 students were referred to the RTI problem-solving team.

Figure 2
Universal Screening Class Results
First Grade

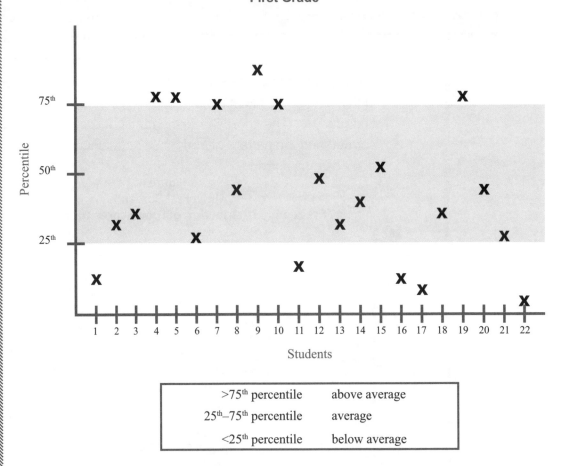

>75th percentile	above average
25th–75th percentile	average
<25th percentile	below average

The Source for RTI
Copyright © 2008 LinguiSystems, Inc.

▶ **Diagnostic Assessments**

Diagnostic assessments determine what students can and cannot do in specific academic and behavioral domains. Diagnostic assessments measure students' current knowledge and skills for the purpose of identifying what students may need to accelerate learning.

Diagnostic assessments are most informative when they

- measure predetermined core learning objectives;
- are systematically embedded into the curriculum;
- identify the next steps for teaching and learning;
- are used to give specific feedback to students;
- indicate modifications to the scope and sequence of the curriculum.

In some situations, a group-administered diagnostic assessment can be given to students who are struggling in the classroom to identify specific skills that need more instructional attention. In other situations, an individual diagnostic assessment is administered that is skills-based, curriculum-based, and linked directly to grade-level expectations. These test results should identify specific skills that a student needs to learn with extra support. Finally, if more comprehensive information is needed about the student's learning profile, referral for special education evaluation can be initiated.

▶ **Progress-Monitoring Assessments**

Progress monitoring is a scientifically validated process that is used to assess students' academic performance and to evaluate the effectiveness of instruction. It helps us

- estimate amount and rate of student progress on target skills in the curriculum;
- identify students who are not making adequate progress and may need additional support;
- pinpoint when to adjust or improve instruction or intervention to meet students' needs.

Progress monitoring is effective when performance is measured frequently enough to provide the desired information. It is also effective when it yields quantitative data so that student progress can be graphed and viewed relative to the learning goals. Progress monitoring can be used with individual students, an entire class, or an entire grade level in a school or district.

Three Steps in RTI Progress Monitoring

1. The teacher determines each student's current levels of performance on core educational skills that contribute to success in school.

2. The teacher or school team identifies goals and monitors progress by comparing actual rates of learning with expected rates of learning.

3. The school team reviews the progress-monitoring data to determine if they need to make adjustments to the instruction or intervention.

Curriculum-Based Measurement (CBM) is a well-researched form of RTI progress monitoring (Deno & Mirkin 1977; Deno 1985; Shinn 1989). CBM is a way of tracking and recording a student's progress in specific areas (e.g., math, reading, writing, spelling). Teachers regularly assess their students' performance using brief, simple test probes. CBM has several important features:

- Direct measurement of core academic skills and behaviors
- Repeated measurement
- Time series analysis (i.e., measure growth in performance over time)

Stanley Deno and Phyllis Mirkin, along with their colleagues at the University of Minnesota, developed the Curriculum-Based Measurement approach. This approach has its roots in the Data-Based Program Modification model created in the late 1970s for making educational decisions for students in special education.

When using CBM, a teacher tests students with quick probes that last from one to five minutes. The teacher counts the number of correct and incorrect responses in the allotted time to find a student's score. For example, the teacher may ask the student to read aloud for one minute. A reading fluency check may consist of number of words read correctly in one minute. The teacher then calculates the score and enters it on a graph. With this approach, both the student's performance in the curriculum and rate of progress in mastering the curriculum can be compared to expected performance in that skill for that time of year. (See Figure 3 below.)

Figure 3
Curriculum-Based Measurement
Student Profile Relative to Class Peers

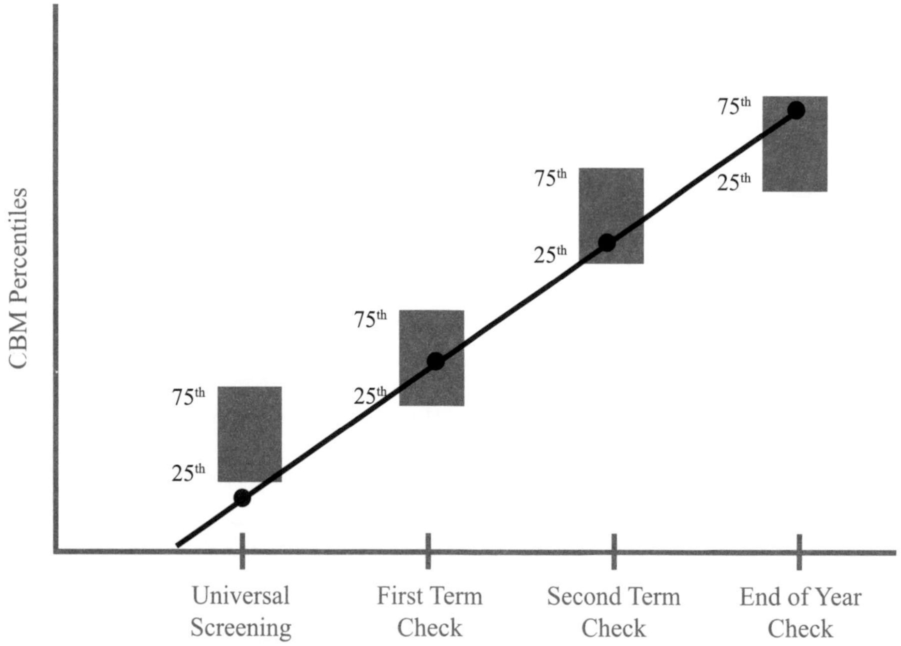

In this example, the student scored below the 25th percentile on the universal screening at the beginning of the year and was provided with Tier 1 support in the classroom. The student scored in the average range (between the 25th and 75th percentiles) on periodic progress monitoring.

Following the progress-monitoring probes, the teacher, parent, and school team can use the data for making changes. Progress monitoring in an RTI system has several advantages over traditional norm-referenced assessments and other informal measures of student performance:

- Based on the curriculum
- Individually referenced (a student's performance is compared to his/her own performance over time)

- Peer referenced (a student's performance is compared to same-grade peers)
- Useful for making instructional decisions
- Sensitive to student growth and improvement
- Time efficient and cost effective
- Tied to standards

Examples of Curriculum-Based Measurement Tools

Dynamic Indicators of Basic Early Literacy Skills (DIBELS)
http://dibels.uoregon.edu

AIMSweb
http://www.aimsweb.com

Monitoring Basic Skills Progress (MBSP)
http://www.proedinc.com

Yearly Progress Pro
http://www.mhdigitallearning.com

Integrated Data Management Systems

Three-Tier RTI integrated data systems are the platform for RTI decisions. They should have the following characteristics (NASDSE 2006):

- Directly assess specific skills in state and local academic standards
- Sensitive to small increments of growth over time
- Can be administered efficiently over short periods
- May be administered repeatedly (using multiple forms)
- Can be summarized in teacher-friendly data displays
- Can be used to make comparisons across students
- Can be used to monitor an individual student's progress over time
- Have direct relevance to providing instruction and intervention that address each student's area of need

There is a 30-year history of development and research about integrated data collection and data assessment systems affecting decisions in a Three-Tier RTI model (Deno 1985; Shinn 1989; Howell & Nolet 2000). The Office of Special

Education Programs in the U.S. Department of Education funded a national program to support development and dissemination of information regarding progress monitoring and data-driven decisions. (For more information about data-driven decisions go to http://www.studentprogress.org/default.asp.)

Data in a Three-Tier RTI Model

▶ **Tier 1 Core Instruction Data**

At Tier 1, universal screening, diagnostic assessment, and periodic progress monitoring answer two questions:

1. **How is this student doing compared to other students?**

   State and federal accountability systems use end-of-year testing data in the spring of the year to make programming decisions for students who are struggling with grade-level material. Universal screening and periodic monitoring assessments in the RTI framework provide a better option. Using a student's response to the instruction and performance on curriculum-based measures can help determine (1) if the student is making the expected progress for grade level or (2) if the student needs more intensive support and intervention.

   If data from universal screening, diagnostic assessments, and periodic progress monitoring show that a particular student is struggling in Tier 1, a recommendation is made for a Tier 2 intervention.

2. **Is the Tier 1 instruction effective so that at least 80 percent of the students achieve district benchmarks?**

   Administrators and RTI teams can gauge how effective the curriculum and instruction is for students. The team analyzes the effectiveness of the curriculum by looking at the mastery levels, instructional levels, and frustration levels of classes at the same grade level in the school or in the district.

   If the majority of the students perform well below grade-level instruction, there will be a high level of frustration. The pace and sequence of the curriculum should be adjusted.

   If one class scores noticeably lower on the screening and progress-monitoring assessments than other classes at the same grade level, the problem is likely with the instruction and can be addressed with professional development.

▶ **Tier 2 and 3 Data**

At Tier 2 and Tier 3, data about a student's response to intervention is collected through frequent progress monitoring. It provides information to answer three questions:

1. **Is the student learning the expected amount of material to master the target skill/s or behavior/s?**

   At Tiers 2 and 3, frequent progress monitoring helps determine if there is a "good" response to the intervention. A good response to the intervention would be the gap closing between the student's performance and the average range of performance expected on the target skill.

2. **Is the student making the expected rate of progress on the target skill/s or behavior/s?**

   Intervention is not effective for a student if the gap continues to widen between the student's performance and average performance for the skill. When an intervention is not effective, it should be discontinued. Instead, a different intervention can be provided at Tier 2 or at Tier 3 (with increased intensity, frequency, and duration).

3. **Are the fidelity and efficacy of the intervention adequate?**

   Intervention must demonstrate fidelity as well as efficacy. **Fidelity** means that the staff provides the intervention in the way that it was designed. For example, if the intervention protocol requires that the student move through three learning stations of 10 minutes each but there is only time in the session to go to two learning stations, then the fidelity of the intervention is compromised. Without fidelity, efficacy cannot be evaluated.

   Tier 2 intervention is provided in small groups using standard protocols (i.e., the same intervention for all of the students in the group). Progress monitoring of the target skill/s may be included with the intervention program/approach or may be customized by the district. Some progress-monitoring probes may be administered individually, and some probes may be administered to the group.

   Progress monitoring for Tier 3 intervention is very frequent, matched to the target skill/s and administered individually. Frequent progress monitoring at Tier 3 is essential for insuring that the intervention is effective and provides the needed support for the student to move into the average range of performance.

The SLP's Role in RTI Data

▶ **Tier 1 Data**

- Help identify screening measures that are sensitive, specific, and designed to sort students who probably have delays from students who probably don't. (See Screening Tests Analysis Worksheet, appendix E1, page 114. For a completed form, see appendix E2, page 115.)

- Assist with universal screening (administration, scoring, analysis of group and individual results), pointing out trends and patterns for certain classes or grade levels.

- Conduct expanded screening for articulation and language deficits. Provide speech and language screening to students who fail selected language-related items on the universal screening. For example, a student with very poor reading comprehension for grade level may have a weak language learning system. Expanded screening for a language deficit may provide information about the most effective type of Tier 2 intervention.

- Participate in data analysis about school performance. Closely examine the results for students below the 10th percentile to determine which students may be struggling due to a weakness in speech and/or language.

▶ **Tier 2 and Tier 3 Data**

- Help identify progress-monitoring procedures that facilitate data-driven decisions.
- Graphing student progress is one of the easiest ways to analyze and share student progress information. Graphs create a learning picture, help predict learning, provide documentation, and make data easier to interpret. (See the figures below and on page 46. Figure 4 shows monitoring of articulation progress relative to correct production of the target phoneme. Figure 6 shows monitoring of progress on language targets relative to progress in the curriculum.)

Figure 4
Student Progress Chart – Tier 2 Intervention
Articulation Target: /r/ in all word positions

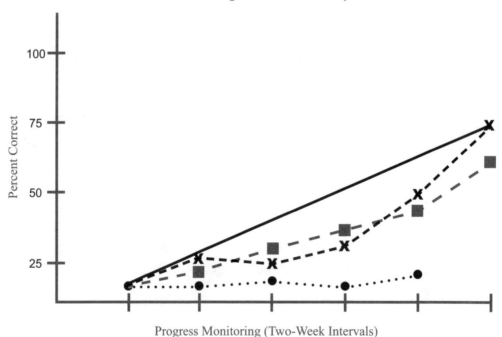

Progress Monitoring (Two-Week Intervals)

—— Aim Line: Reach 75% accuracy for target in 10 weeks

X Outcome: This student met target objective in 10 weeks.

● Outcome: This student did not meet target objective. Change Tier 2 intervention or ask problem-solving team to consider referral for speech evaluation.

■ Outcome: This student did not meet target objective but is making steady progress. Continue Tier 2 intervention.

Figure 5
Student Progress Chart – Tier 3 Intervention
Language Targets: correct use of pronouns, possessive pronouns, and pronoun-verb agreement

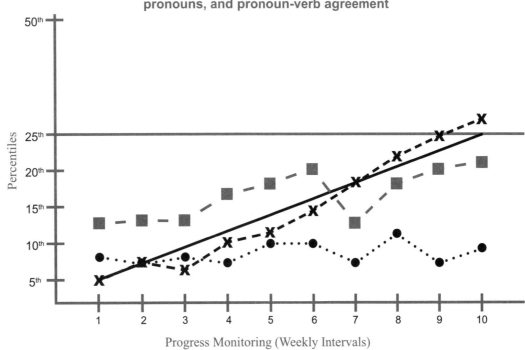

Progress Monitoring (Weekly Intervals)

—— Aim Line: Reach 25th percentile on curriculum-based assessment

X Outcome: This student met target objective in 10 weeks.

● Outcome: This student did not meet target objective of 25th percentile and gap is not closing between performance and grade-level expectations. Ask problem-solving team to consider referral for language evaluation.

■ Outcome: This student did not meet target objective but gap is closing (getting closer to 25th percentile).

Students exit Tier 2 or 3 intervention when performance in the curriculum is above the cut score. In this example, it would be the 25th percentile.

- Participate in determining cut scores and developing local norms at your school.

  Ideally, cut scores are developed statistically on a significant amount of data collected over time. If the cut score is set too high, then a larger group of students will be identified as at-risk and in need of Tier 2 or Tier 3 intervention. If the cut score is set too low, students who truly need the intervention may be missed.

  For example, if cut scores are set at a performance level of the 25th percentile, about 25 percent of the school population will be identified as needing Tier 2 or Tier 3 intervention (assuming in this example that the school or district reflects national norms). This rate is somewhat higher than the target rate of 80 percent of students' needs being fully met in Tier 1 instruction and about 20 percent of students needing Tier 2 or Tier 3 intervention. At the 25 percent level, 6 or 7 students out of a class of 25 students will be identified for Tier 2 or Tier 3 intervention.

  If the 25 percent level strains a district's resources, it may be more feasible to set a cut score using the 10th percentile based on district norms or school norms. This cut score allows for 2 or 3 students per class of 25 to receive Tier 2 or Tier 3 intervention.

Computing Percentile Ranks

Percentiles are frequently used in education as a type of rank score. There are several statistical methods for computing percentiles. Essentially, they are obtained by computing the percentage of scores that fall below a given raw score. For example, if 50 percent of the scores are at 14 or below, then a score of 14 is at the 50th percentile.

1. Enter scores for each student on a spreadsheet.

2. Use a statistics calculation program such as SPSS and specify percentiles (e.g., 25th, 50th, 75th).

3. Chart class results to determine which students scored below the percentile designated by the school or district as the cut score.

Websites for Computing Percentiles

http://www.mfe.govt.nz/issues/water/hazen-percentile-calculator.xls

http://www.psychstat.missouristate.edu/IntroBook2/sbk12.xml

- Apply the concept of RTI data-driven decisions to monitoring the progress of students on your caseload. Graph progress results and compare progress in therapy to the expected rate of progress for the skill. Discuss actual progress and expected progress with the student, parents, and teachers.

RTI and a Problem-Solving Process

Dynamic problem-solving processes are essential to the integrity of RTI. Analysis of data for the purposes of improving instruction, aligning curriculum to state standards, and making informed decisions about intervention for individual students is necessary for RTI to meet student needs.

RTI Problem-Solving Teams

Schools should designate one or more teams to problem-solve as needed within the RTI framework. Building an intervention team is complex and takes time. Team membership, priorities, functioning, behaviors, beliefs, and leadership are the important variables for successful RTI problem-solving teams. Large schools may designate more than one RTI problem-solving team. For example, one RTI team might handle school-wide and systemic issues related to curriculum and delivery of instruction, and other teams might handle student-specific issues.

There are a variety of ways to establish school teams, but the staffing of the RTI team should be determined by the needs of the student or the problem at hand. Teams usually have at least three members with a maximum of seven members. Some of these members can be alternates.

RTI problem-solving team members share the following characteristics:

- Committed to the school's instructional goals
- Willing to accept responsibility for the progress of all students in the school
- Experienced and skillful in providing a variety of teaching strategies and intervention
- Experienced in analyzing and interpreting data
- Respected by other staff
- Good listeners
- Attentive to the sensitive and confidential nature of RTI discussions

Depending on the nature of the problem, core team members include the principal and the referring teacher, as well as an instructional specialist, counselor, or master classroom teacher. Other team members may include specialists with expertise in addressing the problem, such as the SLP, school psychologist/behavioral specialist, nurse, social worker, or other classroom teachers (especially those with positive, successful relationships with the student).

RTI problem-solving teams create the impetus for realigning traditional roles and responsibilities. For example, SLPs or school psychologists have not traditionally had a big role in prevention and early intervention activities. By participating in RTI problem-solving teams, these professionals have the chance to contribute to student and school improvement in a new way.

Much of the team's effort revolves around student performance data:

- Determining what data are needed (e.g., screening results, baseline data, progress-monitoring data, group assessment data, individual assessment data)
- Gathering the data
- Organizing the data
- Summarizing and analyzing the data
- Meeting regularly to determine efficacy and fidelity of instruction and intervention
- Defining learning problems in measurable terms
- Developing intervention plans
- Exploring research-based intervention
- Providing immediate, relevant, hands-on support to the classroom teacher
- Reviewing data reports on intervention and student progress
- Interviewing referring individuals
- Using data to make additional recommendations
- Evaluating response to intervention
- Documenting meeting deliberations

The RTI problem-solving team leader is usually the principal. Leadership by the principal defines the success of the RTI process as a whole and of the problem-solving team in particular. Implementing an RTI model in the school will cause change in the school culture and among the faculty and staff. The school change and educational leadership literature emphasizes that any change in a school must be "accepted, appreciated, and nurtured by the principal" (Hord 2004). The school principal provides leadership for RTI and the team problem-solving process with vocal support, resources, and active participation on the team.

Time is a valuable commodity in schools, and is one of the resources largely under the principal's control. Establishing a time to meet is one of the most important factors for sustaining a successful team (Boyd 1992). The other resources and support that teams need include: communication structures, protocols, and tools to manage the work (e.g., forms and simple procedures for documenting team discussions).

RTI Problem-Solving Process

Problem solving in an RTI framework involves four repeating activities in an upward spiral of continuous improvement.

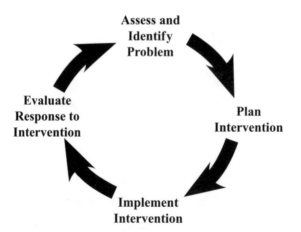

1. **Assess and identify the problem.** During this phase of the process, the problem-solving team uses data to identify and describe the problem. Concerns may be related to delivery of the curriculum and instruction or related to individual student academic achievement or behavior. The team describes the problem in specific, observable, and measurable terms.

2. **Plan the intervention.** The team uses data to plan adjustments to the curriculum scope and sequence or to the delivery of instruction in a classroom or grade level. The team may also plan which level of intervention is most likely to meet individual student needs. The plan outlines who will do what, when, and how. The plan specifies a goal and how to monitor progress toward the goal.

Intervention plans should include the following (McCook 2006):

- Baseline data describing student performance on the target skill/s
- Description of the specific intervention provided
- Duration, frequency, and schedule for the intervention
- Person responsible for implementing the intervention
- Measurable outcomes
- Rubric or plan for adjusting the intervention if needed
- Schedule of progress monitoring
- Schedule for review of student progress data

---

3. **Implement the intervention.** Teachers or other school staff implement the plan for systemic improvements or for support for individual students through specialized intervention.

4. **Evaluate student response to the intervention.** The team uses student performance data from assessments and progress monitoring to evaluate responses to changes in the instruction or intervention. At this phase of the process, the team determines if the plan worked.

Three-Tier RTI Problem Solving

The RTI problem-solving process can be applied at several levels to address different types of problems.

Individual students: academic and/or behavior problems

Classroom: situations when delivery of curriculum and instruction need to be adjusted, or when classroom-specific issues need attention (e.g., homework not turned in, poor discipline management, low student morale, poor attendance by many of the students in the class)

Campus: school-wide issues (e.g., bullying, poor student attendance across classrooms, poor teacher attendance)

District: systemic issues (e.g., widening achievement gaps between disadvantaged and advantaged students)

In addition, the problem-solving process can be used to make decisions at each tier of the RTI framework.

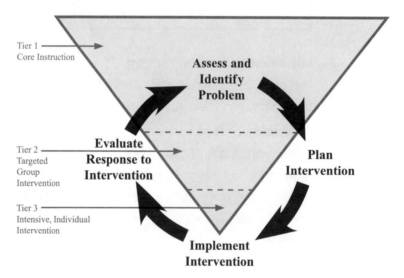

The RTI Model of Student Support (appendix F, page 116) provides a flowchart that incorporates this process across tiers.

There are several decision-making points along the path of support. At each decision point, the problem-solving team reviews data to determine which students are responding to the instruction/intervention and which students are not.

▶ **Tier 1 Core Instruction**
The problem-solving team looks at results of universal screening, diagnostic benchmark assessments, and periodic progress monitoring. When fewer than 80 percent of the students make the expected progress, the team uses a problem-solving process to address the issue. It may be necessary to make adjustments to the scope and sequence, pace of instruction, or alignment of the district's curriculum with state standards.

When instruction is satisfactory for at least 80 percent of students in every classroom, problem solving is directed toward those students who struggle to meet academic and behavior expectations for grade level. This process can occur at any time throughout the year.

Although Tier 1 problem solving is data-driven, it is less formal than other levels of problem solving. For example, if a teacher has concerns about an individual student's academic achievement or behavior, the teacher and parents meet informally. Together they identify the problem, agree on a plan, and monitor progress. Then they meet for a follow-up conference to review the effectiveness of the informal intervention.

If the student's problems persist or if the student does not meet expectations on periodic curriculum benchmarks, a more formal problem-solving process is initiated. The teacher or parent requests assistance from the problem-solving team to determine if the student needs additional Tier 1 support or a Tier 2 intervention. The team develops an individual intervention plan to provide the level and intensity of support needed to help the student meet grade-level expectations.

The problem-solving team may also identify students who need additional support as they review screening and benchmark assessment results for each grade level.

Communication with parents about their child's performance at school and about additional support provided in an RTI framework is critical to student success. If the problem-solving team identifies an individual student to receive focused intervention, it is important that the teacher communicate this information to the parents.

▶ **Tier 2 and Tier 3 Intervention**

The problem-solving team reviews student performance data and the expectations outlined in a student's intervention plan to measure responsiveness to instruction/intervention. Students who respond well to targeted group intervention and catch up with grade-level expectations can exit Tier 2 and have their needs fully met in the classroom. For students who do not respond adequately to the intervention, the problem-solving team uses student performance data to decide if the intervention has been provided with fidelity and integrity. If so, the team may recommend the same intervention with more frequency and intensity through Tier 3. If not, they may recommend a different intervention through Tier 2 or Tier 3.

At Tier 3, the problem-solving team continues to use student performance data from frequent progress monitoring to make decisions about continuing the intervention, pulling back the intensity of support after the student has made good progress, or making a referral to special education.

The RTI Model of Student Support is designed to solve problems through general education so that all students benefit fully from Tier 1 instruction. Adequate student support is provided when student performance data is available and when the problem-solving team uses a consistent problem-solving process.

Problem Solving and the SLP

SLPs can participate in the RTI problem-solving process in a variety of ways, depending on the needs of the students and the school. One of the keys to effective and consistent problem solving is a set of decision-making rules to help guide decisions. The team may specify local norms (e.g., below the 10th percentile) for determining when to consider students for Tier 2 intervention. The team may also specify a decision-making rule for intervening with a teacher (e.g., when 30 percent or more of the students in a class do not perform well on a benchmark assessment).

The critical time to use data decision rules are for: (1) making effective decisions about when to continue, change, or stop a particular intervention for individual students and (2) making consistent decisions to implement a school's RTI framework. SLPs have the type of training and expertise to assist the problem-solving team with developing and monitoring these decision rules.

▶ **Problem-Solving Team Activities**

- Volunteer to participate on the school-wide RTI problem-solving team to look at global school issues or to participate on student RTI problem-solving teams to support students struggling in the classroom.

- Participate on the problem-solving team to review Tier 1 assessment results. When needed, provide support and technical assistance to teachers about the language basis of literacy and grade-level language demands in the curriculum.

- Participate on the problem-solving team to support students who need Tier 2 or Tier 3 intervention by giving your input about which intervention is most likely to meet a student's needs. Call attention to situations in which speech and language development may be a contributing factor to low performance.

- Work with the problem-solving team to establish a progress-monitoring system prior to starting an intervention for students. Various data collection methods are available (e.g., percent correct, number correct per time unit, demonstrated skill correctly 10 times over 3 sessions). Some intervention programs have data collection methods embedded in their programs. Refer to appendix G, page 117, for help in developing a progress-monitoring system.

- Reflect on the team process and any professional development the team may need to improve its effectiveness. Team support is important and can happen through specific training about the team problem-solving process, team member roles and responsibilities, consensus, and how to analyze data to make effective decisions for students. Encourage ongoing professional development about the RTI problem-solving team process.

- Help your team keep it all in perspective. How does your problem-solving process interface with RTI assessment activities? How do RTI activities interface with comprehensive individual evaluations? Refer to the RTI Problem-Solving Crosswalk: Data Driven Decisions, appendix H, page 118.

▶ **Data Decision Rules**

- Work with your team to develop and use data decision rules to evaluate effectiveness of intervention for each student. Refer to Basic Steps for Developing Data Decision Rules, appendix I, page 119.

- Pay close attention to the data decision rules for interventions that are heavily loaded for speech and language skills. Provide input on expected rate of progress in the acquisition of speech, language, and communication skills.

- Track the data decision rules over time and assist your team in adjusting the rules when needed. For example, the team may review campus data and determine that 15 percent rather than 10 percent of students with the lowest scores on periodic curriculum assessments should receive Tier 2 intervention.

- Give input to the team about developing school norms for data decision rules. An example set of data decision rules follows on the next page (McCook 2006). Note that your problem-solving team may decide on different percentiles for continuing, changing, or stopping an intervention.

Tier 1

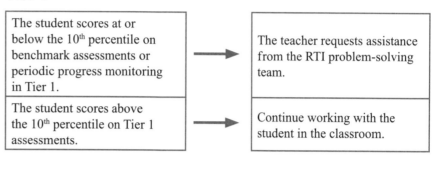

The student scores at or below the 10th percentile on benchmark assessments or periodic progress monitoring in Tier 1.	The teacher requests assistance from the RTI problem-solving team.
The student scores above the 10th percentile on Tier 1 assessments.	Continue working with the student in the classroom.

Tier 2

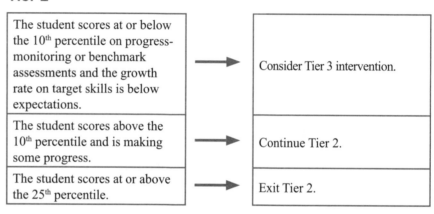

The student scores at or below the 10th percentile on progress-monitoring or benchmark assessments and the growth rate on target skills is below expectations.	Consider Tier 3 intervention.
The student scores above the 10th percentile and is making some progress.	Continue Tier 2.
The student scores at or above the 25th percentile.	Exit Tier 2.

Tier 3

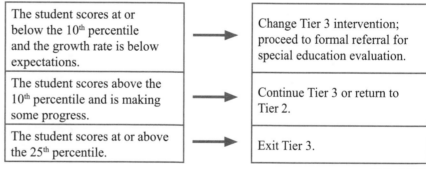

The student scores at or below the 10th percentile and the growth rate is below expectations.	Change Tier 3 intervention; proceed to formal referral for special education evaluation.
The student scores above the 10th percentile and is making some progress.	Continue Tier 3 or return to Tier 2.
The student scores at or above the 25th percentile.	Exit Tier 3.

McCook 2006

▶ **Manage Data to Make Decisions**

- See appendixes J and K1, pages 121-123 for examples of RTI problem-solving team forms. Page 124 shows a completed progress-monitoring form.

RTI and Special Education Eligibility Determination

There is growing support in policy and in the literature for moving away from reliance on a discrepancy formula and moving toward an identification model that involves scientifically-based response to intervention (Bradley, Danielson, & Hallahan 2002). In fact, the final regulations for IDEA 2004 went above and beyond the language of the law to endorse the use of RTI in identifying disabilities.

> Models that incorporate response to a research-based intervention should be given priority in any effort to identify students with specific learning disabilities. Identification models that incorporate response to intervention represent a shift in special education toward the goals of better achievement and behavioral outcomes for students identified with specific learning disabilities [Federal Register: June 21, 2005 (Volume 70, Number 118, 35781-35892)].

RTI Evaluation Procedures

With over half of all students in special education identified with a learning disability, the option to use RTI models for evaluation purposes has far-reaching implications. RTI models include the capacity for substantive changes to traditional methods and procedures that determine eligibility for special education and related services. RTI models are designed to address student needs quickly and efficiently. Students are not identified for special education services until they have first received quality instruction and support in general education. RTI emphasizes monitoring students' progress in instruction and intervention, which provides rich information and an added dimension to the data collected during individual evaluations for eligibility determination.

In a three-tier model, when a student does not respond to Tier 2 or Tier 3 intervention, the parent, teacher, or problem-solving team may request a referral to special education. At that time, a variety of data about the student is available:

- Screening results
- Progress-monitoring data
- Documentation of differentiated strategies
- Type and fidelity of intervention

- Rate and amount of progress in response to different interventions
- Environmental conditions that support or hinder the student's learning

The parents, the problem-solving team, and the multidisciplinary evaluation team should use all available information to help them answer three questions that will determine whether or not to make a special education referral. (See the Referral for Special Education Evaluation, appendix L, page 125.)

1. **Were the interventions matched to the student's needs, delivered with sufficient intensity, and implemented with fidelity?**

2. **Given the student's response (or lack of response) to intervention, do we suspect that the student might have a disability?**

3. **Are there other questions we need to answer before we can determine if there is a disability?** For example, the student may demonstrate intense instructional need with gaps in learning, but show the expected rate of learning with Tier 3 intervention. Questions about English language proficiency should be addressed.

If the answer to question 1 or 2 is **"no,"** the student continues to receive Tier 2 or Tier 3 intervention with frequent progress monitoring and support for learning in the regular classroom.

If the answer to question 3 is **"no,"** the RTI data provides most or all of the evidence needed to document a learning disability and the need for special education and related services in order to make progress in the general curriculum. RTI data can be used to complete the full individual evaluation eligibility report.

If the answer to all three questions is **"yes,"** the RTI information is not sufficient to document a language or learning disability. In this case, the multidisciplinary team completes a comprehensive individual evaluation.

Comprehensive Individual Evaluation Process

IDEA 2004 spells out the process for conducting a comprehensive individual evaluation.

▶ **Review existing data.**

First, the multidisciplinary team plans the evaluation by reviewing information about the child's educational, health, and developmental history:

- Evaluations and information from a parent
- Current classroom-based, local or state assessments
- Classroom-based observations
- Observations by teachers and related service providers
- Responsiveness to intervention data

▶ **Obtain additional data.**

Next, the multidisciplinary team obtains any additional data needed to determine whether the child has or continues to have a disability requiring special education and related services. In conducting the evaluation, the multidisciplinary team must use a variety of assessment tools and strategies to gather relevant functional, developmental, and academic information about the child [300.304 (b)].

These assessment activities may include gathering additional information from the parent and the teacher, reviewing samples of student work, direct testing activities including standardized tests, informal tests, and targeted observations. Comprehensive evaluations address the following areas:

- Physical/motor/medical
- Cognitive development and adaptive behavior
- Educational performance and achievement
- Sociological
- Communication
- Emotional and behavioral

▶ **Interpret the data.**

Following assessment, the multidisciplinary team interprets the data, taking the following into account:

- Aptitude and achievement tests
- Parent input
- Teacher recommendations
- Information about the child's developmental and functional performance and adaptive behavior
- Information about the child's social or cultural background

The team uses results from the evaluation and information from parents, teachers, and the student in the following ways:

- Identify the cause/s of the limited response to intervention
- Determine whether the student has a disability that results in an adverse effect on educational performance
- Design an IEP to help the student make progress in the general curriculum (i.e., if a disability that results in an adverse effect on educational performance is documented)

RTI and LD Determination

The following framework is available from the Rhode Island Department of Education (Hauerwas & Woolman 2006) for using RTI data instead of traditional testing to identify students with LD. (See the Identification of Learning Disabilities flowchart, appendix M, page 126.)

▶ **Document learning needs.**

Does evidence from a variety of sources indicate that the student's learning needs are greater than 90 to 95 percent of grade-level peers? Use the dual discrepancy model (Fuchs 2003) to help determine whether a student has a learning disability.

Discrepancy 1: Level of Performance
The student performs academically or behaviorally at a level that is significantly below peers and below grade-level expectations.

Discrepancy 2: Rate of Learning
Despite one or more well-designed, well-implemented interventions, the student fails to close the gap with classmates.

When a student does not respond to Tier 2 or Tier 3 intervention or responds at a slower rate than expected, the greater intensity, frequency, and duration of intervention in special education and related services may help the student make progress and return to classroom instruction (only).

▶ **Consider exclusion factors.**

After careful review, can we rule out any other primary causes for the student's distinct needs? IDEA 2004 specifies that the following must be ruled out as primary causes of the student's learning difficulties to be eligible for services:

- Visual, hearing, or motor disability
- Mental retardation or emotional disturbance
- Cultural factors
- Environmental or economic disadvantage
- Limited English proficiency
- Lack of appropriate instruction in reading or math

▶ **Document adverse impact of learning difficulties on education.**

Does the student need special education and related services in order to meet his or her needs? In order to answer "yes," the student must require instructional intensity at a level greater than 90 to 95 percent of grade-level peers, and the exclusion factors mentioned above must be considered.

When the multidisciplinary team has the documentation to answer "yes" to all three issues, there is evidence of an underlying learning disability and verification of its adverse impact on educational performance. The student would then be eligible for special education services. RTI data can be used to complete the full individual education eligibility report.

If the data shows that any one of the conditions is not present (i.e., the answer to one or more of the questions above is "no"), a learning disability and eligibility for special education is not established. In this case, any intervention at Tier 2 or Tier 3 should be modified to better fit the student's needs.

Advantages of RTI in Referral and Evaluation Activities

RTI strengthens the child-centered evaluation process in several important ways:

- RTI results in significantly fewer referrals for special education evaluation. Students who respond well to Tier 2 and Tier 3 intervention close the gap in their achievement and return to Tier 1 classroom instruction (only) without needing referral to special education.

- RTI eliminates "insufficient instruction" as a factor that may have caused a student's learning problems (i.e., when high-quality instruction and intervention have been provided through a multi-tier RTI model).

- RTI may prevent placement in special education. Effective instruction and empirically-based intervention cannot prevent a language or learning disability. For some students, however, the appropriate instruction/intervention can reduce the disability's adverse effect on educational performance so that special education and/or related services are not required.

- RTI information makes the comprehensive evaluation process more sensitive and robust in terms of meaningful results for the student.

- RTI information helps identify patterns of abilities and helps individualize instruction when used with information from the comprehensive evaluation of the student's cognitive ability/processing strengths and weaknesses.

- RTI data directs future instruction for a student in a more sensitive way than data generated by ability-achievement discrepancy testing.

- RTI data helps guide development of the individualized education program (IEP).

- RTI information helps the multidisciplinary team pay attention to individual differences between students (inter-individual comparisons) and within students (intra-individual comparisons).

IDEA 2004, RTI, and Speech-Language Evaluations

Nationwide, 20 percent of the six million school-age students in special education are coded speech-language impaired (only). Over 50 percent of students in special education are coded with a learning disability and many of these students are also coded with speech or language impairment. The number of students with language-learning disabilities may well be close to four million. SLPs can effectively use RTI models for identification, prevention, and intervention with these students who struggle with language-based learning.

▶ **RTI and Referrals for Speech-Language Evaluation**

When the school uses a multi-tier RTI model, the SLP can follow the same protocol for referrals as discussed on pages 64-65. In an RTI framework, it is vital that concerns about the student's speech and language skills be grounded in how these difficulties may contribute to the student's struggle in the classroom. The SLP uses RTI data to answer these referral questions relative to communication disorders:

- Have the interventions been matched to the student's needs, delivered with sufficient intensity, and implemented with fidelity?
- Have the interventions been provided to improve suspected speech or language difficulties that may contribute to struggle in the classroom?
- Given the student's response to these focused interventions, do we suspect that the student might have a communication disorder?
- Are there other questions we need to answer before we can determine if there is a communication disorder?

▶ **RTI and Determining Speech-Language Impairment**

In school settings, no one person determines whether or not a child has a disability. IDEA 2004 specifies that evaluations to determine eligibility for special education and related services, including speech and language services, fall under the responsibility of a multidisciplinary team and a parent. "A group of qualified professionals and the parent of the child determine whether the child is a child with a disability" [Sec 300.306(a)(1)].

Further, students must be assessed in all areas of suspected disability with a comprehensive evaluation that identifies all the child's special education and related services needs, whether or not commonly linked to the disability category in question [Sec. 300.304(4) and Sec. 300.304(c)(6)]. RTI information helps the SLP meet these IDEA 2004 requirements for comprehensive evaluations because of its strong emphasis on student performance in the classroom and responsiveness to focused intervention.

RTI data and/or comprehensive speech-language evaluations describe academic, functional, and developmental communication skills and provide sufficient information about the student's communication for the IEP team to answer three questions:

1. Is there evidence of a communication disorder?
2. Is there an adverse effect on educational performance resulting from the communication disorder?
3. Does the student require specially designed instruction or related services to make progress in the general education curriculum?

Each of these questions will be explained in more detail below.

1. **Is there evidence of a communication disorder?**

   RTI information is very powerful in differentiating between a communication delay, a communication difference, and a communication disorder. For example, when a student responds quickly and well to a Tier 2 language intervention, it is likely that the basis for concern was a language delay rather than a language disorder. On the other hand, if a student responds well to additional time and exposure to explicit instruction in English, it is likely that the basis for concern was a language difference rather than a language disorder.

   In both situations, RTI serves as a means of preventing student failure. Some students struggle to meet grade-level standards in Tier 1 instruction due to language delay or language difference. When provided with a Tier 2 intervention that meets their particular needs, the students are able to catch up and then keep up with their peers.

If concern exists after Tier 2 or Tier 3 intervention is provided along with Tier 1 instruction, a referral is initiated for an individual speech and language evaluation. If a communication disorder is identified using valid methods for assessment, then a disability condition exists and the second question should be answered.

If a communication disorder is not documented, the disability condition is not present and the student is not eligible for special education services under the eligibility category of speech or language impairment. The student may, however, continue to receive Tier 2 and/or Tier 3 intervention through RTI.

Delay—Difference—Disorder

A **communication delay** exists when the rate of acquisition of language or speech skills is slower than expected according to developmental norms, yet the sequence of development follows a predicted order (Nicolosi, Harryman, & Kresheck 1989).

A **communication difference** is a "variation of a symbol system used by a group of individuals that reflects and is determined by shared regional, social, or cultural/ethnic factors. A regional, social, or cultural/ethnic variation of a symbol system should not be considered a disorder of speech or language" (ASHA 1993, p.2).

A **communication disorder** is impairment in the ability to send, receive, process, and comprehend verbal, nonverbal, and graphic symbol systems. A communication disorder may be evident in the process of hearing, language, or speech; may be developmental or acquired; and may range in severity from mild to profound (ASHA 1993).

---

2. **Is there an adverse effect on educational performance resulting from the communication disorder?**

    Progress-monitoring results for Tier 2 and Tier 3 intervention provide important information for answering this question. The level of performance for the target skill/s or behavior and the rate of improvement in Tier 2 or Tier 3 intervention are key.

IDEA 2004 regulations [Sec 300.8 (c)(I)(1)] define a speech or language impairment as "a communication disorder, such as stuttering, impaired articulation, a language impairment, or a voice impairment that adversely affects a child's educational performance."

Deciding whether the communication disorder has an adverse effect on educational performance involves documenting its effect on both academic achievement and functional performance. **Academic achievement** generally refers to a child's performance in academic areas, such as reading or language arts, math, science, and history. **Functional performance** refers to skills or activities that are not considered academic or related to a child's academic achievement. This term is often used in the context of routine activities of everyday living [Federal Register, 71(156), p. 46661].

academic achievement
+
functional performance
_____

educational performance

In addressing the effect of the communication disorder on **academic achievement**, the SLP identifies curriculum contexts in which the student struggles because of the communication disorder. The SLP then uses those contexts to determine how the student's disordered communication impedes learning and designs future intervention to address communication skills within the context of the curriculum (Nelson 1994).

The SLP evaluates **functional performance** of speech and language skills by describing communicative competence in the classroom, in nonacademic settings, and in extracurricular activities. Effective communication skills are essential for activities in the classroom (discussions, oral reports, presentations) and in social interactions outside of the classroom (peer interactions; conversations with adults; participation in concerts, plays, or special programs) (ASHA 2007).

If there is a disability condition resulting in an adverse effect on educational performance, then the IEP team examines the third question.

3. **Does the student require specially designed instruction or related services to make progress in the general education curriculum?**
   In an RTI model, the critical question for special education and related services is the same as for Tier 2 and Tier 3 intervention: What type of intervention results in change? Special education becomes an alternative for students who don't respond to Tier 2 or Tier 3 intervention and who need the power, flexibility, and often extended frequency, intensity, and duration of IDEA services. In the RTI framework, speech and language services are provided when a student has a communication disorder that adversely affects his or her educational performance (i.e., to the point of needing specially designed instruction or related services and supports in order to make progress in the general curriculum).

RTI and the SLP

There are several ways SLPs can use RTI data for making eligibility recommendations to the IEP team. Suggestions are provided in this section for blending RTI activities with communication assessment and evaluation activities.

▶ **Base evaluations on a communication model.**
   Consistent, sensitive, and accurate diagnostic decisions are essential. Speech and language therapy services through special education hinge on the identification of a communication disorder. Use a communication model, such as appendix N on page 127, to help ground your evaluation activities for making consistent decisions about whether or not a student demonstrates a communication disorder. Depending on state regulations and guidelines, a communication model may be adopted at the state or school district level. In either case, RTI data can be effective in making decisions about supporting students in Tier 2 or Tier 3 speech and language intervention/IEP services by using a communication model to examine communication skills in school environments.

▶ **Include RTI data in referral information.**
RTI data, especially a student's response to Tier 2 or Tier 3 intervention, can help shape a referral to special education as well as reduce the amount of individual testing needed to complete the comprehensive evaluation. In the sample referral form (appendix O, pages 128-133), record RTI data under Referral Information (section I) and the Educational Learning Competencies (Academic Performance) (section VIII). Note the comparison to expected grade-level performance and rate of learning with intervention on pages 131-132. These are two important variables in the RTI framework.

All of the referral and RTI information is available to the SLP as a member of the multidisciplinary team and is helpful for planning the speech-language evaluation activities. For example, the SLP uses the referral concerns, language proficiency information, and academic and behavior RTI performance data to form hypotheses about the student's communicative competence relative to grade-level academic and behavioral expectations.

▶ **Incorporate RTI principles into the planning process.**
Most students referred for comprehensive individual evaluation should have data available about their responsiveness to Tier 2 and Tier 3 intervention. Careful consideration of this data helps the multidisciplinary team determine how much, if any, additional testing is needed to answer the three eligibility questions listed on page 71.

The Multidisciplinary Team Planning Form for Individual Student Evaluation (appendix P, pages 134-136) is an example of an action plan for completing a comprehensive evaluation when referring a student for special education consideration.

▶ **Use a decision-making rubric.**
Consistent reference to a decision-making rubric may help you describe the adverse effect of the communication disorder on educational performance. It may also help you match interventions through RTI and/or special education and related services to students' needs. A sample rubric, explaining the effect on educational performance in terms of academic achievement and functional performance, is provided in appendix Q on pages 137-138.

▶ **Use a workload approach to schedule evaluation activities.**

ASHA's Workload Implementation Guide (2003) contains information and guidance for using a balanced workload approach to provide quality speech and language services in schools. One of the most powerful tools available for SLPs to maximize use of RTI with students—flexible scheduling— emerged from ASHA's Workload Approach. Flexible schedules allow SLPs to vary their schedules from week to week in a patterned rotation. (A sample flexible schedule is provided in appendix D on pages 112-113.)

Using a flexible schedule approach allows the SLP to schedule RTI activities, other early intervening services, and assessment and evaluation activities on different days of the week and different times of the day from week to week.

Flexible schedules and RTI go hand in hand. Dedicate time in your schedule for the following range of RTI/assessment activities.

- Observe classroom Tier 1 instruction. Note whether any students seem to struggle with the language complexity of the content, instructions for completing work, or reading level of books in the classroom.

- Observe students in Tier 2 and Tier 3 intervention to collect information on response to intervention as it relates to language and the curriculum.

- Observe and assess students' communication skills in the classroom and other academic and nonacademic settings, including extracurricular activities.

- Complete individual evaluations of students referred for speech and/or language concerns.

- Participate on RTI problem-solving teams to evaluate students' responsiveness to intervention when speech and/or language contribute to the student's struggle.

- Implement Tier 2 intervention with a student as diagnostic information in the 60 days following referral (i.e., the designated time frame for completing evaluations).

RTI and Speech and Language Services

SLPs are well equipped to define quality speech and language services within a multi-tier system. There are important roles and responsibilities for SLPs throughout the RTI framework that contribute to the three-prong purposes of RTI: prevention, identification, and intervention. This chapter describes the range of direct and indirect speech and language services in relation to student services provided in a three-tier RTI model.

Tier 1: mostly indirect services to support quality instruction in the classroom and to participate in prevention activities

Tier 2: a combination of direct intervention and indirect services

Tier 3: mostly direct intervention and identification services

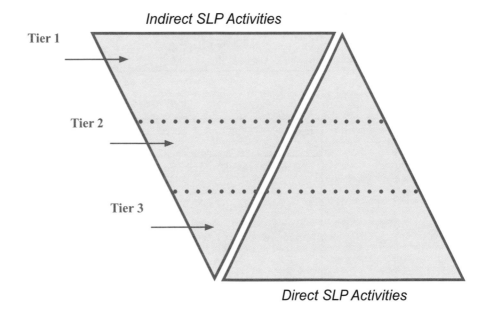

Tier 1 Core Instruction

▶ **Student Services**

Two types of assessment data are collected for all students in Tier 1 to gather information about the students' response to instruction and progress through the curriculum:

- Universal screening at the beginning of the year
- Periodic progress monitoring three or four times per year

▶ **Data Decision Rules**

Districts and campuses using a three-tier RTI model develop data decision rules to facilitate consistent decision making. SLPs should be familiar with these decision-making protocols in order to participate fully in supporting students both "inside" and "outside" of special education. The following is an example of decision points and the role of the SLP in Tier 1.

Universal Screening

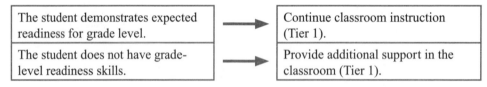

The student demonstrates expected readiness for grade level.	Continue classroom instruction (Tier 1).
The student does not have grade-level readiness skills.	Provide additional support in the classroom (Tier 1).

Periodic Progress Monitoring

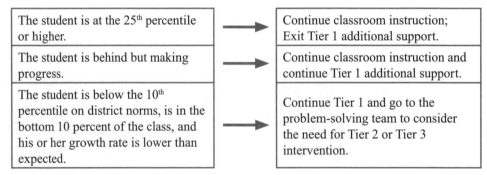

The student is at the 25th percentile or higher.	Continue classroom instruction; Exit Tier 1 additional support.
The student is behind but making progress.	Continue classroom instruction and continue Tier 1 additional support.
The student is below the 10th percentile on district norms, is in the bottom 10 percent of the class, and his or her growth rate is lower than expected.	Continue Tier 1 and go to the problem-solving team to consider the need for Tier 2 or Tier 3 intervention.

Expanded Speech-Language Screening

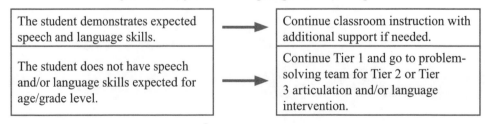

The student demonstrates expected speech and language skills.	Continue classroom instruction with additional support if needed.
The student does not have speech and/or language skills expected for age/grade level.	Continue Tier 1 and go to problem-solving team for Tier 2 or Tier 3 articulation and/or language intervention.

▶ **SLP Activities at Tier 1**

The SLP may provide some direct services in the classroom and a variety of indirect services to support quality instruction in the general education classroom:

Direct services include activities such as conducting expanded speech and language screening or providing support for struggling students through a variety of classroom activities.

Indirect services include completing student observations, helping the teacher make connections between oral language and literacy, and providing staff development to improve teachers' understanding and delivery of instruction that is matched to students' language learning needs. Indirect services are designed to prevent more serious communication problems in the future.

Direct Services

Expanded speech and language screening

There are three options for the expanded screening:

1. *Teacher report with SLP observation*

   Using an SLP-provided rating form or checklist (appendix R, page 139), the teacher rates the articulation and/or language skills of the students who scored below expectations on the universal screening and the first progress-monitoring benchmark. In addition, the teacher may also provide information about students who are making expected progress in the curriculum, but who have noticeable articulation errors for age or grade level.

   The SLP observes the students receiving additional Tier 1 support and conducts quick stimulability checks for correct production of errors in speech production and/or language use. Students who are stimulable for correct production continue receiving Tier 1 support. Students who are not stimulable for correct production may benefit from Tier 2 articulation and/or language intervention.

2. *District-developed screening test*

   School districts can develop articulation and language screening tests and collect data to establish local norms for age and grade level. Locally developed screening measures have the highest reliability when combined with teacher report. The use of district norms and the use of cut scores for making decisions about the level of support students need to perform at expected levels fits in well with an RTI model.

3. *Published speech and language screening test*

   A good screening test should be norm-referenced, valid, reliable, sensitive, specific, short, easy to administer and score, and easy to interpret. (Refer to ASHA's 2007 directory of assessments for a listing of published tests.)

Direct SLP support

Additional support in the classroom often consists of the following:

- Spending extra time working on the material the students are struggling with
- Organizing small, flexible groups with multiple opportunities for interaction
- Tutoring during the school day
- Modifying the presentation of information

Difficult material should be presented in a variety of ways with multiple opportunities for active learning (hands-on activities, thinking and discussing, applying concepts).

- Several school districts have started programs that support students who struggle with expressive language skills. These programs use the RTI framework with a Tier 1 classroom co-teaching model (Dunaway 2006; Wiechmann & Balfanz 2007). The approach uses story frames and story grammar to support students in their language arts curriculum by strengthening narratives, questioning skills, and written expression. The teacher and SLP provide explicit, structured teaching about telling and writing stories.

The SLP focuses on oral language skills and the teacher focuses on written language skills. Using scaffolding and modeling, they take a simple, straightforward story and expand and extend detail through questioning techniques so that the final story is interesting and has a point. As a result, students produce their own stories, practice the questioning techniques to help others add detail to their stories, write their own stories, and eventually read their stories to the class.

The benefits of this co-teaching model include understanding the main idea, practice asking and answering relevant questions, experience with the use of story structures for expository writing, and more descriptive language with improved skills in expressing feelings and emotions. This type of Tier 1 support is a good fit in grades two, three, and four. The emphasis is on oral language for the younger students and written language for the older students.

These are examples of other ways SLPs provide direct support in the classroom:

- Scheduling classroom time during small group instruction to work with students who have difficulty with speech or language development
- Assisting students in kindergarten and first grade with "good speech" in socio-dramatic play centers, listening centers, or speech centers
- Providing classroom lessons that promote effective communication behavior and connections between oral and written language

Indirect Services

The wide range of indirect RTI service delivery available in Tier 1 allows the SLP to participate in prevention activities as well as contribute to quality instruction in the classroom.

Classroom observations

Observations of the whole class provide information about students' response to instruction and progress in the curriculum. SLPs may assist the school team and the classroom teacher in analyzing language demands of the curriculum and the effects of those demands on students. (See Language Demands of the Curriculum—Analysis Worksheet, appendix S1, page 140. For an example of a completed worksheet, see appendix S2, page 141.)

Individual student observations provide information about response to instruction with specific information about where a breakdown in learning occurs (points in the curriculum or instructional delivery). The SLP and teacher may rate students' communication skills and compare ratings for a more complete profile about students who seem to struggle with the language basis for learning. (See Language Demands of the Curriculum—Teacher Observation, appendix T1, page 142 and Language Demands of the Curriculum—SLP Observation, appendix U1, page 144. See pages 143 and 145 for examples of completed forms.)

School improvement teams

When possible, SLPs should be regular members of the campus RTI problem-solving team. This team's decisions directly affect the range of activities covered in an SLP's workload—from RTI prevention and intervention activities to assessment, evaluation, and IEP caseload assignments. Other campus teams involved in prevention activities include literacy teams, child study teams, and curriculum committees. RTI models allow more opportunities for the SLP to become an active team member who is responsible for student achievement.

Parent education

SLPs can be involved in parent education, especially in explaining the connections between language and literacy and providing milestones for typical speech and language development. The SLP can also provide parents with information and activities to help support their student's speech and language development.

Homework programs

When a student has simple articulation errors and is stimulable for correct production, the SLP can provide Tier 1 support with a homework program to practice correct production of error sounds. Arrange a parent and student conference to explain the program, get agreement from parents, and set up a schedule for the student to turn in homework and monitor progress. (See Articulation Practice Record, appendix V, page 146.)

Curriculum and instruction consultation

In order to participate effectively in RTI, SLPs must become familiar with state performance standards, the district's curriculum for addressing state standards, and effective instructional practices for teaching the curriculum. In particular, a natural "niche" for the SLP's expertise is providing information to teachers about the language demands in the standards and the curriculum, and how to use language to meet students at their level.

Staff development

Staff development is the key to rigorous, high-quality classroom instruction (Tier 1), which in turn drives effective multi-tier RTI models. SLPs have an important role to play in providing and participating in staff development, either in a traditional workshop or a professional learning community format (DuFour, DuFour, Eaker, & Karhanek 2004). SLPs have specialized information about language and literacy connections and can provide staff development on the following topics:

- Strategies for teaching literacy-based skills (e.g., the alphabetic principle, decoding and spelling, later vocabulary development, roots and prefixes)
- Matching instruction to students' language learning needs
- Aligning language in the curriculum with language of instruction
- How to increase the complexity of students' oral and written communication while teaching the content
- Grade-level expectations for listening, speaking, reading, and writing

Tier 2 Targeted Group Intervention

▶ **Student Services**

- Students enter Tier 2 at two points: (1) when additional support in the classroom does not fully meet their learning needs to keep pace with grade-level expectations and (2) when periodic progress monitoring in Tier 1 shows the students are performing below the campus or district cut score.

- Students in Tier 2 receive frequent progress monitoring (every two to three weeks) on target skills to provide information about their response to Tier 2 intervention.

- Tier 2 students also participate in Tier 1 periodic progress monitoring that gives information about their response to instruction and progress through the curriculum.

▶ **Data Decision Rules**

The data decision rules at Tier 2 guide recommendations for one of the following options:

- Exit Tier 2 to Tier 1 only instruction.
- Continue Tier 2 intervention.
- Exit Tier 2 for additional intervention in Tier 3.
- Make a special education referral.

Examples of decision points in Tier 2 and the role of the SLP follow on the next page.

Frequent Progress Monitoring

The student is at the 25th percentile or higher.	Exit Tier 2.
The student is behind but is making progress.	Continue Tier 2 (consider changing intervention).
The student is below the 10th percentile on district norms, is in the bottom 10 percent of the class, and his or her growth rate is lower than expected.	Go to the problem-solving team for Tier 3 consideration or special education referral.

Tier 2 Articulation Intervention with Frequent Progress Monitoring

The student corrects error sounds to 75 percent accuracy.	Exit Tier 2.
The student is making progress but not at 75 percent accuracy.	Continue Tier 2.
The student is not making noticeable progress.	Go to the problem-solving team for Tier 3 consideration or special education (speech) referral.
The student is not making noticeable progress, oral-motor issues are noted, or a phonological disorder is suspected.	The problem-solving team considers a referral to special education (speech).

Tier 2 Language Intervention with Frequent Progress Monitoring

The student is at the 25th percentile or higher on classroom progress monitoring and shows expected performance on target language skills.	Exit Tier 2.
The student is behind but is making progress.	Continue Tier 2 language intervention (consider changing intervention).
The student is below the 10th percentile on district norms, is in the bottom 10 percent of the class, and his or her progress rate in Tier 2 language intervention is lower than expected.	Go to the problem-solving team for Tier 3 consideration or special education referral.

▶ **SLP Activities at Tier 2**

The SLP provides direct articulation and language intervention for students whose speech or language skills are not at expected levels.

Direct services include targeted group intervention to support students' articulation and language skills in small, same-ability groups.

Indirect services include helping to select research-based literacy interventions, completing student observations and assisting with frequent progress monitoring of Tier 2 literacy intervention, and helping the problem-solving team make decisions on how best to meet student needs.

Direct Services

Tier 2 articulation and language intervention programs include the essential components of other RTI Tier 2 interventions:

- Focused intervention on specific skills
- Intervention provided in addition to Tier 1 instruction
- Small, same-ability groups of up to four students
- Frequent progress monitoring
- Frequent intervention

Articulation

There are several RTI articulation intervention models available (Taps 2006; Dunaway 2006; Wiechmann & Balfanz 2007) with more models emerging into accepted practice. Effective Tier 2 articulation intervention includes these basic parameters:

- A speech screening and/or teacher report identify students who may benefit from Tier 2 articulation intervention.
- Errors consist of simple sounds and are not attributed to phonological processes, dialectal differences, learning English as a second language, or language deficits.
- Parents are provided with information about the articulation intervention.

- Intervention includes completing word and sentence probes, drawing the students' attention to error sounds, modeling correct production, providing placement cues, and practice of correct production through drills.

- Students work in groups of three to four or rotate through stations where each student plays a game or performs motor movements while repeating the target sound (in isolation, words, or phrases).

- Students' productions of the target phonemes are monitored each session. Students may rotate through a station where they monitor and chart their own productions of the target phonemes.

- Sessions are scheduled for 30 minutes, two to four times per week.

- Districts develop cut scores for exiting Tier 2 articulation intervention.

Language and literacy

Tier 2 language intervention programs either continue the additional language support provided in Tier 1 (e.g., story frames and story grammar) in a more structured format with increased frequency or provide focused intervention to remediate language deficits contributing to the student's struggle with grade-level curriculum.

Tier 2 language intervention includes these basic parameters:
- A language screening and/or teacher report identify students who may benefit from Tier 2 language intervention.

- Concerns about language development are not attributed to dialectal differences or learning English as a second language.

- Parents are provided with information about the language intervention.

- Intervention includes focused activities to strengthen listening, speaking, reading, and writing skills.

- Students work in groups of three to four or rotate through language stations.

- Sessions are scheduled for 30 minutes, two to four times per week.
- Districts develop cut scores for exiting Tier 2 language intervention (similar to the exit criteria for struggling readers).

Indirect Services

In Tier 2, indirect SLP services shift from Tier 1 systemic (school-wide) prevention activities to prevention activities that support individual students. Indirect RTI services may include these types of activities:

- Helping to select research-based or evidence-based literacy interventions
- Observing Tier 2 students in the classroom to identify when struggle may be linked to speaking, listening, reading, or writing skills
- Assisting Tier 2 service provider with frequent progress monitoring
- Communicating progress in Tier 2 articulation or language intervention to parents and teacher
- Participating on the RTI problem-solving team to make decisions about when students enter and exit Tier 2 intervention

Tier 3 Intensive, Individualized Intervention

▶ **Student Services**

- A student may enter Tier 3 at two points: (1) when the student is very behind in the classroom or (2) when the student's response to Tier 2 intervention is not at the expected rate or level.
- Students in Tier 3 receive very frequent progress monitoring on target skills to provide information about their response to Tier 3 intervention.
- Tier 3 students also participate in Tier 1 periodic progress monitoring that gives information about their response to classroom instruction and progress through the curriculum.

▶ **Data Decision Rules**

The data decision rules at Tier 3 guide recommendations for one of the following options:

- Exit Tier 3 to Tier 1 (only) instruction.
- Exit Tier 3 to less intensive or reduced frequency intervention in Tier 2.
- Continue Tier 3.
- Discontinue Tier 3 in lieu of specially designed instruction through special education.

The following is an example of decision points and the role of the SLP in Tier 3.

Very Frequent Progress Monitoring

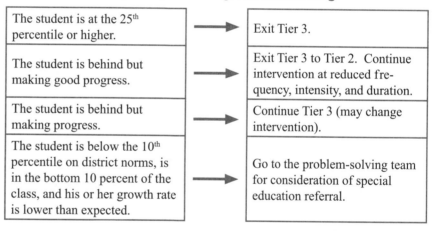

The student is at the 25th percentile or higher.	Exit Tier 3.
The student is behind but making good progress.	Exit Tier 3 to Tier 2. Continue intervention at reduced frequency, intensity, and duration.
The student is behind but making progress.	Continue Tier 3 (may change intervention).
The student is below the 10th percentile on district norms, is in the bottom 10 percent of the class, and his or her growth rate is lower than expected.	Go to the problem-solving team for consideration of special education referral.

(continued on page 90)

Tier 3 Articulation Intervention with Very Frequent Progress Monitoring

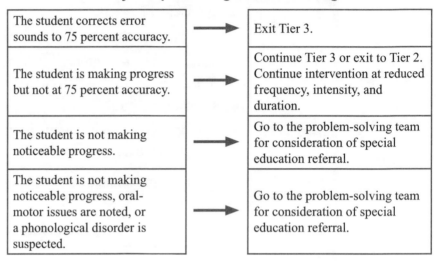

The student corrects error sounds to 75 percent accuracy.	Exit Tier 3.
The student is making progress but not at 75 percent accuracy.	Continue Tier 3 or exit to Tier 2. Continue intervention at reduced frequency, intensity, and duration.
The student is not making noticeable progress.	Go to the problem-solving team for consideration of special education referral.
The student is not making noticeable progress, oral-motor issues are noted, or a phonological disorder is suspected.	Go to the problem-solving team for consideration of special education referral.

Tier 3 Language/Literacy Intervention with Very Frequent Progress Monitoring

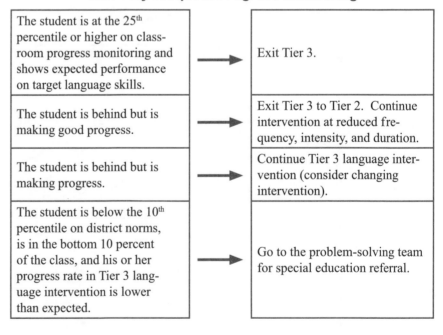

The student is at the 25th percentile or higher on classroom progress monitoring and shows expected performance on target language skills.	Exit Tier 3.
The student is behind but is making good progress.	Exit Tier 3 to Tier 2. Continue intervention at reduced frequency, intensity, and duration.
The student is behind but is making progress.	Continue Tier 3 language intervention (consider changing intervention).
The student is below the 10th percentile on district norms, is in the bottom 10 percent of the class, and his or her progress rate in Tier 3 language intervention is lower than expected.	Go to the problem-solving team for special education referral.

▶ **SLP Activities at Tier 3**

The SLP provides direct, intensive articulation and/or language intervention for students whose speech and/or language skills are not at expected levels. The SLP closely monitors the amount and rate of their progress on target skills. She uses this information to determine when to make a referral for a special education evaluation. A special education evaluation can help provide complete information about a student's communication skills and language learning system. The SLP also provides some indirect services to support students receiving other Tier 3 literacy interventions.

Direct services include intensive, individualized intervention to support students' articulation and language skills.

Indirect services include helping to select research-based literacy interventions, completing student observations in Tier 3 intervention, assisting with frequent progress monitoring of Tier 3 literacy intervention, and helping the problem-solving team make decisions regarding referral for special education evaluation.

Direct Services

Tier 3 articulation and language intervention programs include the following essential components of other RTI Tier 3 interventions:

- Focused intervention on specific skills
- Intervention provided in addition to Tier 1 instruction
- Intensive, individualized intervention
- Very frequent progress monitoring
- Very frequent, longer intervention

Articulation and language

The SLP carefully monitors students who do not make good progress in Tier 2 articulation or language intervention to determine if a referral to special education for a comprehensive speech and language evaluation is warranted. When an individual evaluation shows that an articulation or language disorder is not present and that specially designed services through special education are not needed, Tier 3 articulation or language intervention may provide the level of support a student needs to make expected progress in the classroom. Tier 3 articulation and language intervention is similar to Tier 2 intervention, but it is provided more frequently (five times per week), for longer periods of time (30- to 60-minute sessions), and for longer duration (more weeks).

Language and literacy

Montgomery and Moore-Brown (2005) developed a Tier 3 language and literacy intervention program. It includes these components:

- Designed for elementary students who are struggling with reading
- A nine-week, 45-hour evidence-based program (one-hour sessions, five days per week)
- Sessions focus on the five building blocks of reading (phonemic awareness, phonics, reading fluency, vocabulary comprehension, reading [text] comprehension)
- Groups of same-ability students
- Very frequent progress monitoring
- The SLP and reading specialist share responsibility for implementing the program. The SLP focuses on phonemic awareness and vocabulary and the reading specialist focuses on phonics, reading fluency, and comprehension.
- Students who don't make the expected progress in nine weeks are considered for special education referral.

Identification of communication disorders

One of the three primary purposes of RTI is effective and sensitive identification of students with high-incidence disabilities (i.e., learning disabilities and speech or language impairment). When students do not make the expected amount or rate of progress in Tier 3 articulation or language intervention, a request for special education/speech and language evaluation is appropriate.

RTI provides dynamic assessment data about a student as a learner. With parent permission, the SLP uses information about how the student responds to Tier 3 articulation or language intervention to shape further evaluation or intervention activities. This information also helps the SLP determine whether the student's difficulty with speaking, listening, reading, and/or writing meets eligibility requirements for special education through IDEA. A distinct advantage of using RTI data in a dynamic assessment approach is that it yields information that is typically limited in static assessment. RTI allows the SLP to plan meaningful intervention to meet the student's needs.

Static assessments take a snapshot of student performance at one point in time, on one set of criteria, administered in a prescribed way. Standardized tests and performance-based assessments (e.g., language sample, student products, video-recorded performance) are types of static assessment.

Dynamic assessments examine student performance under varying conditions in an interactive manner to determine the type and degree of assistance needed for the student to be successful. This test-teach-retest approach emphasizes the learning process the student is using, not the learning that has already occurred.

Indirect Services

In Tier 3, indirect SLP services center around supporting students with particular attention to identifying students who may need referral to special education for comprehensive evaluation. Indirect RTI services at Tier 3 may include these activities:

- Helping to select research-based or evidence-based literacy interventions
- Observing Tier 3 students in the classroom to identify when struggle may be linked to speaking, listening, reading, or writing skills
- Assisting Tier 3 service provider with very frequent progress monitoring
- Participating on the RTI problem-solving team to make decisions about when students enter and exit Tier 3 intervention
- Participating on the RTI problem-solving team to make decisions about referral to special education (e.g., providing information that can be used in a dynamic assessment model)

Communication with Parents in an RTI Model

A major concern for parents is how to help their children as they experience difficulty learning and fall behind in academics or demonstrate behaviors that disrupt learning. In the past, children experiencing the most difficulty were referred for evaluation to determine eligibility for special education. With the hope of preventing more serious learning difficulties, the RTI framework provides opportunities to communicate with parents early and to seek their involvement and participation.

Consider the following opportunities throughout the RTI process for communicating with parents:

- Inform parents about RTI and the procedures in place for supporting students who experience difficulty with academics or behavior.

- Include information about speech and language services in the information about RTI that is provided for all parents at the school.

- Inform parents when expanded speech and language screening is needed and follow up with information about results of the screening measures. If a child fails the screening, discuss possible next steps for supporting the student with academics, speech and/or language development, or behavior.

- Inform parents about results of the progress monitoring conducted with all students in Tier 1 instruction.

- Provide home activities for children who show signs of difficulty keeping pace with classroom instruction.

- Include parents in monitoring home practice of articulation skills for Tier 1 or Tier 2 intervention.

- Provide information for parents about Tier 2 or Tier 3 intervention. Follow district protocols for obtaining parent permission for these supplementary services.

- For students who are not performing at expected levels, invite parents to participate in a teacher conference or in the problem-solving team discussion to plan Tier 2 or Tier 3 intervention.

- Provide progress-monitoring results to parents. Communicate with parents about progress in Tier 2 or Tier 3 speech and/or language intervention.

The Source for RTI
Copyright © 2008 LinguiSystems, Inc.

- Provide the required informed notice and consent for special education referral and evaluation when needed. The procedural safeguards are in place for students and parents when a referral for special education is initiated.

- Keep parents in the loop. IDEA 2004 requires that parents be provided with data about their children's performance on periodic assessments reflecting progress or lack of progress during instruction.

RTI, Systems Thinking, and Continuous Improvement

The U.S. Department of Education and state education agencies encourage and require documentation of continuous improvement efforts. State education agencies and school districts submit continuous improvement plans for improving or sustaining high levels of student performance in special education, Title I, and other programs funded through No Child Left Behind (NCLB). One premise of continuous improvement as the framework for planning and decision making in schools is **systems thinking**, the process of seeing the big picture and the connections between all parts of the whole (Turner 2007).

A **system** is a set of related parts that receives input, adds value to it, and produces output to achieve a defined purpose or goal (Turner 2007). Systems such as schools are made up of parts or subsystems that interact and are interrelated.

> **RTI can be the mechanism that allows two parts (general and special education) of the system (school) to work together to improve teaching and learning for all students.**

Recognizing the connections and interdependency of the subsystems is a critical feature of using a systems orientation to maximize effectiveness in the organization. When special education and general education work interdependently, the whole system (school) maximizes effectiveness for reaching the defined purpose or goal. RTI can be the mechanism that allows two parts (general and special education) of the system (school) to work together to improve teaching and learning for all students.

Case Study: Irving ISD

These are the essential ingredients for using the core principles of RTI for systemic school improvement:

- Strong district and campus leadership for RTI
- RTI "housed" in general education, not special education
- Effective Tier 1 instruction in every classroom
- Tier 2 and Tier 3 intervention for all students, including those in special programs
- Data-driven staff development

- Resources allocated to support research-based Tier 2 and Tier 3 intervention programs
- Procedures and infrastructure to support instruction and data collection

Figure 1 shows an integrated RTI framework in a school district in which all students have access to instruction and intervention at all tiers in a three-tier system.

Figure 1
An Integrated RTI Framework at Work

Used with permission—Irving Independent School District

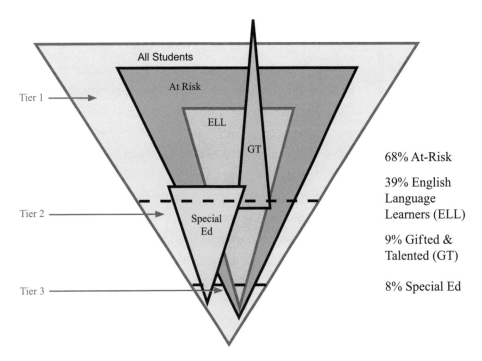

The district shown in figure 1 is a suburban district in north Texas with an enrollment of nearly 33,000 students. Students in the district are 67% Hispanic, 16% White, 12% African American, and 5% Asian and Other. Seventy-two percent of the students are economically disadvantaged and qualify for free or reduced lunch. In terms of special populations, 39% of the students are English language learners (ELLs) and there are 53 languages represented in the district with the largest number of ELLs (92%) speaking Spanish as their first language. Nine percent of the students are identified as gifted and talented (GT), and 8% of the students are in special education programs. Sixty-eight percent of the students are considered at risk of dropping out of school.

Texas established 13 indicators that place a student at risk for dropping out, ranging from poor academic performance with failing grades, retention, or not passing state assessments to social, emotional, and behavioral factors (e.g., discipline infractions, homelessness, unstable home environments). English learners who are coded as Limited English Proficient (LEP) are considered at risk. For the most part, at-risk status is fluid and students can move out of this category if they demonstrate sustained improved academic and behavioral performance or English proficiency. State compensatory education funds are available for districts to accelerate learning for students considered at risk in order to close the achievement gap between advantaged and disadvantaged learners.

Figure 1 shows that all students have access to instruction and intervention in Tier 1, Tier 2, or Tier 3 as needed. This includes students who are already placed in a special program, such as bilingual education or special education. Note that the ELL students are fully contained within the at-risk triangle, and that there is overlap between students who are coded at risk, GT, and special education. The district uses an accelerated academics model for GT, so the triangle spikes above Tier 1 to depict that students in these classes may be performing above grade level. There are students who receive GT services, who are learning English and coded LEP, and who also have a disability and an individualized education program (IEP) through special education. Students identified as GT, who also have a disability, are referred to as "twice exceptional." Teaching and learning systems are significantly challenged when the student is twice exceptional and learning English as a second language.

The district depicted in figure 1 took the following action to develop an integrated RTI system:

▶ **Leadership**

- District leadership for teaching and learning (including the superintendent and assistant superintendent) articulated a vision and commitment to the RTI framework with the school board, principals, and various stakeholder groups in the district (e.g., district improvement committee, parent advisory council).

- The district's three-tier RTI model for supporting students is a general-education initiative with an expectation for principals to work proactively to meet the needs of all students at the school.

- District staff took time to study RTI models, assist in identifying research-based interventions for Tier 2 and Tier 3, and articulate how initiatives already in place to improve classroom instruction would fit into an integrated three-tier RTI system.

- Information about the three-tier RTI model is provided to the school board on a regular basis, with information about RTI woven into instructional reports.

- Principals provide campus leadership for RTI instruction and intervention with careful attention to routine analysis of student performance data and to modeling the problem-solving component of the system.

▶ **Effective Tier 1 Instruction**

- Effective instruction of a standards-based curriculum is a prerequisite to successful use of an RTI approach. The district has worked in a continuous improvement manner since 2004 to provide a teacher-developed, online curriculum. The district's curriculum provides a scope and sequence for instruction of the state standards. Teacher teams work during the summer and periodically during the school year to review, revise, and improve the district's curriculum.

- Tier 1 instruction should fully meet the needs of 80-90% of the students. The expectation for highly effective instruction applies to specialized classes, including special education, bilingual education, English as a Second Language (ESL), Title 1, and gifted and talented. If a student's primary instruction is through a specialized classroom, that class is considered the Tier 1 instruction and must be aligned with standards and the district's curriculum.

- Staff development supports effective classroom instruction and is designed based on student performance data. Staff development systems have been implemented in the district based on the standards from the National Staff Development Council (2003). Since effective staff development is critical to student success, these systems are differentiated to meet the needs of novice and experienced teachers. Over fifty percent of classroom teachers in the district have fewer than five years of teaching experience. With the swelling population of ELLs, the majority of new teachers are bilingual teachers enrolled in alternative certification programs.

▶ **Tier 2 and Tier 3 Intervention Matched to Students' Needs**

- District staff assist campuses in identifying research-based interventions for Tier 2 and Tier 3. Campuses examine the needs of their students and select the intervention approaches that are most likely to be effective.

- Campuses are encouraged to conduct action research and track the effectiveness of locally-developed intervention approaches.

- Tier 2 reading intervention is available in Spanish.

- Tier 2 and Tier 3 reading intervention is available through high school for students with weak reading and literacy skills.

- The needs of students learning English as a second language are systematically taken into account when selecting intervention programs.

- Cross-age reading tutoring approaches are encouraged because of district data showing effectiveness of peer tutoring with students learning English as a second language and students who come from economically disadvantaged homes.

▶ **Resources**

- The district has mechanisms in place to allow for a systems approach to coordinate funding that supports students who are struggling in the classroom. Local, state, and federal funding streams are allocated according to their intent and purpose. The funding sources are scrutinized to reduce duplication of spending and to either accelerate learning for students who are at risk or to provide customized instruction through special programs.

- Title I campuses engage in site-based decision making and use campus data to make decisions about allocation of Title I campus funds.

- The school board has approved additional personnel at each campus to support Tier 2 and Tier 3 reading intervention.

- District staff provides support to campuses by coordinating purchases of Tier 2 and Tier 3 programs, respecting site-based decisions while keeping the whole system in mind.

- District leaders have allocated considerable resources to developing the online curriculum, curriculum-based assessments, and teacher tools (e.g., hand-held devices to collect progress-monitoring data).

▶ **Information Systems**

- The district developed curriculum-based assessments for Tier 1 periodic progress monitoring. Each year, teacher teams add to this bank of curriculum-based questions and probes.

- An electronic student data management system provides information to teachers about each student (e.g., assessment results, grades, at-risk status, English proficiency, student assistance reports).

- Up-to-date teacher tools are available (e.g., PDAs for electronic data collection of progress-monitoring results).

- The staff can record results of student assistance team meetings in the student data management system. In the future, they hope to also capture RTI problem-solving team discussions in this system.

RTI and Continuous Improvement in Special Education

Students with disabilities need intense, explicit, and systematic delivery of services in small groups with consistent monitoring (Torgesen et al. 2001; Fletcher 2006). These features are readily available through an RTI approach outside of special education. But what about students with high-incidence disorders (learning disabilities and speech or language impairment) who are already identified for special education services? Schools and school districts are showing that we can use the principles of RTI to accelerate learning for students with mild disabilities and, in some cases, dismiss them from special education services and fully meet their needs in general education.

The following activities support using RTI for continuous improvement in special education:

- Use special education services as a Tier 2 or Tier 3 intervention. The student receives Tier 1 instruction in the regular classroom and additional support from special education as Tier 2 or Tier 3. For example, resource room or other special education services are provided in addition to Tier 1, not instead of Tier 1. In some situations, attention to the master school schedule and individual student schedules will be needed to achieve this objective.

  - A seventh-grade student might have reading and resource reading in his schedule if additional time is needed to close the gap between current reading level and seventh-grade reading expectations. Resource reading is provided in addition to, not instead of, seventh-grade reading.

  - A fourth-grade student would participate in her regular class for reading and writing. She would go to resource for additional support while other students receive Tier 2 or Tier 3 intervention through general education.

- Use the strategies of specific, target objectives and frequent progress monitoring found in Tier 2 and Tier 3 intervention as part of the special education program. Frequently measure progress in reading and make adjustments to special education services as needed. Do not indefinitely continue special education services that are not effective.

- Use the same RTI problem-solving process for students in special education as other students who are struggling to meet grade-level expectations.

- Turn over accountability for results with students in special education to the grade-level team.

- Review effectiveness of special education services for all students to make decisions about which programs and approaches are most effective for meeting students' needs.

Case Study: Elliott Elementary

Elliott Elementary School is a campus of about 800 students in grades kindergarten through five. Located in the district mentioned on page 99, it is a Title I school-wide campus with 64% of the students eligible for free or reduced lunch. The school has a track record of meeting Title I Adequate Yearly Progress requirements with acceptable ratings in the state accountability system (except for a one-year dip into an unacceptable rating due to fifth-grade science scores).

As RTI and a three-tier intervention model were introduced in the district in 2005-2006, teachers at Elliott Elementary applied RTI principles to instruction in special education.

▶ **First Year**
In 2005-06, the teachers developed an approach to rigorous reading instruction in special education based on the balanced literacy approach used in general education in the district. During the fall 2005 semester, special education teachers at Elliott Elementary formed a professional learning community to review research, visit programs in other districts, and discuss ways to make their special education reading instruction more engaging and effective. With help from district special education staff, they developed an accelerated reading framework to increase the rigor of special education instruction, developed curriculum-based screening and progress monitoring tools, and piloted the program beginning in January 2006. Fifteen students with learning disabilities received Tier 1 instruction and Tier 1 support in the classroom. Special education teachers provided two, thirty-minute additional reading interventions per day.

▶ **Second Year**
In 2006-07, the teachers implemented the accelerated reading program with the 15 students identified for special education with learning disabilities and below grade-level reading scores. Results showed that students who had been making less than a year's progress in a school year averaged about a year and a half of progress during 2006-07. Seven of the students were dismissed from IDEA services with on grade-level reading performance. These results show that the program was meeting the goal of accelerating learning—closing the reading performance gap for students with learning disabilities.

▶ **Third Year**

In 2007-08, the accelerated reading framework approach was continued for students with disabilities. This approach was modified to allow another Tier 2 reading intervention option for students in general education. RTI and a three-tier intervention model appear to be working well for students at Elliott Elementary:

- When students are referred for special education evaluation, there is robust RTI data available to consider during the evaluation and to help plan support for the student.

- Students with mild learning disabilities and language impairment get their needs met in Tier 2 or Tier 3 intervention. Referral and placement in special education is prevented.

- Students who are non-responders in Tier 2 or Tier 3 are quickly referred for special education evaluation. Students identified for special education have more severe learning difficulties and need specially designed instruction through special education for a longer duration.

- The accelerated reading framework effectively meets the needs of students with mild learning disabilities through special education. It is also effective as a Tier 3 intervention for students struggling with reading.

- Elliott Elementary uses a systems approach, collaboration, and RTI problem solving to help meet all students' needs. (See appendix W, page 147-149, for a more detailed description of the accelerated reading framework.)

RTI and Continuous Improvement in Speech-Language Pathology

SLPs can use RTI and a systems approach for continuous improvement of school-based services. SLPs participating in their school's multi-tier RTI approach may find that the following features of RTI add to the quality of speech-language services:

- Direct intervention in Tier 2 or Tier 3 for articulation and language skills may prevent referrals and placement on the caseload. Services are enhanced when appropriate students are identified for SLP services.

- RTI can serve as a bridge between general education and IDEA services, both to prevent referral and placement in special education and to provide intermittent support as needed following dismissal from IDEA services.

- The focused, intensive approaches used in Tier 2 and Tier 3 intervention can be applied to therapy to increase the rate of skills acquisition.

- Data analysis from frequent progress monitoring and the problem-solving process found in RTI add integrity to the system and can be applied with good results to IDEA services.

Wrap-Up

RTI approaches emerged from concerns about over-identification of students with mild, high-incidence disabilities for special education and a wait-to-fail model that placed too much emphasis on assessment and labeling and not enough emphasis on instruction and intervention to address students' learning needs. References to RTI in NCLB and IDEA 2004 show Congressional intent to change the way special education services are delivered in public schools and, in so doing, to reform the entire educational system. RTI models work to address students' problems in the general education arena and prevent more serious problems later on. Since 2001, with the requirements of NCLB in place, there has been a national effort to make schools accountable for the learning of every student.

The RTI systems described in this book use four critical components to improve teaching and learning in schools:

- Instruction and intervention is based on scientifically-based research and matched to state standards.

- A problem-solving approach is used to make data-driven decisions about instruction and intervention with students.

- Intervention is provided at increasing levels of intensity for students who do not meet academic or behavior expectations to insure that students' problems are not primarily due to lack of instruction.

- Progress is monitored frequently to make sure the intervention is effective.

(adapted from NASDSE 2006)

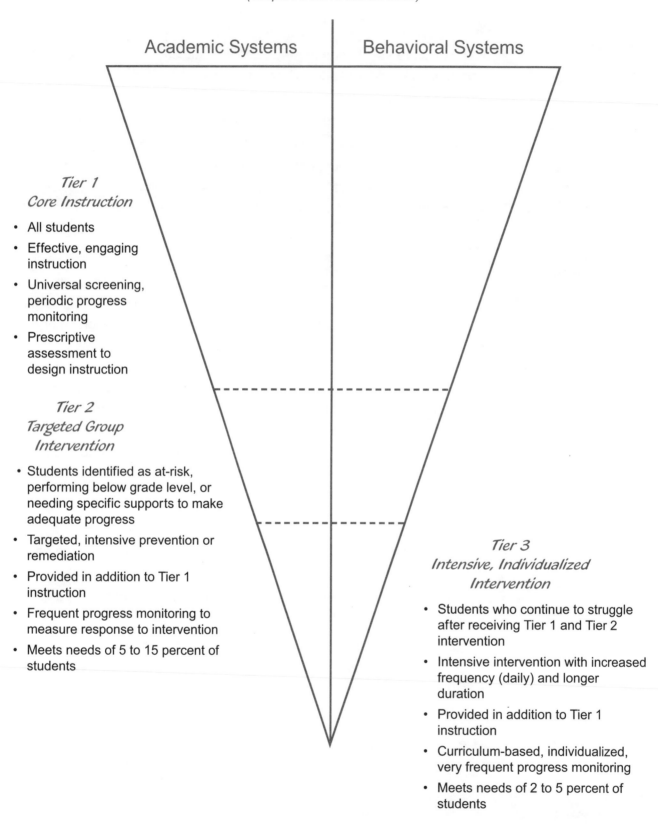

Academic Systems | Behavioral Systems

Tier 1
Core Instruction

- All students
- Effective, engaging instruction
- Universal screening, periodic progress monitoring
- Prescriptive assessment to design instruction

Tier 2
Targeted Group Intervention

- Students identified as at-risk, performing below grade level, or needing specific supports to make adequate progress
- Targeted, intensive prevention or remediation
- Provided in addition to Tier 1 instruction
- Frequent progress monitoring to measure response to intervention
- Meets needs of 5 to 15 percent of students

Tier 3
Intensive, Individualized Intervention

- Students who continue to struggle after receiving Tier 1 and Tier 2 intervention
- Intensive intervention with increased frequency (daily) and longer duration
- Provided in addition to Tier 1 instruction
- Curriculum-based, individualized, very frequent progress monitoring
- Meets needs of 2 to 5 percent of students

Appendix B: Curriculum Correlations for Communication Skills

Grade 2 Language Arts
Taken from Texas Essential Knowledge and Skills (TEKS)

State Standard	Communication Skill	District Scope and Sequence
2.1C	The student will participate in rhymes, songs, conversations, and discussions.	Metalinguistics, Pragmatics, Phonology, Articulation	**Listening/Speaking Objectives** for Units 1 – 6 (all year): Participate in oral language experiences
2.3C	The student will ask and answer relevant questions and make contributions in small or large group discussions.	Semantics, Pragmatics, Syntax	Communicate clearly while speaking appropriately to audiences for different purposes
2.3E	The student will gain increasing control of grammar when speaking, such as using subject-verb agreement, complete sentences, and correct tense.	Syntax	**Reading/Writing Objectives** Unit 2 – Use plural, possessive, and proper nouns; grammar, capitalization, punctuation Unit 3 – Use action verbs, verb tense, use of "have"; sentence
2.4C	The student will retell a spoken message by summarizing or clarifying.	Semantics, Pragmatics	combining; grammar, capitalization, punctuation
2.5 E & F	The student will use structural cues, such as inflections (-s, -es, -ing), prefixes, and suffixes, to recognize compound and base words.	Morphology, Syntax	Unit 4 – Use comparisons; contractions; linking, helping, and irregular verbs; grammar, capitalization, punctuation
2.5G	The student will use knowledge of word order (syntax) and context to support word identification and confirm word meaning.	Syntax, Semantics	Unit 5 – Use pronouns, possessive pronouns, pronoun-verb agreement; contractions; grammar, capitalization, punctuation
2.11J	The student will recognize the story problem(s) or plot.	Semantics	Unit 6 – Use adjectives, adverbs, synonyms, antonyms; grammar, capitalization, punctuation

Grade 3 Mathematics
Taken from Texas Essential Knowledge and Skills (TEKS)

State Standard	Communication Skill	District Scope and Sequence
3.08A The student is expected to identify, classify, and describe two- and three-dimensional geometric figures by their attributes. The student compares two-dimensional figures and three-dimensional figures, or both by their attributes, using formal geometric vocabulary.	Semantics	Unit 13 – Geometry (4th six weeks) Unit 16 – Preview, Extend, Review (6th six weeks)
3.11 The student directly compares the attributes of length, area, weight/mass, and capacity, and uses comparative language to solve problems and answer questions. The student selects and uses standard units to describe length, area, capacity/volume, and weight/mass.	Semantics, Syntax, Morphology	Unit 4 – Measurement (2nd six weeks) Unit 15 – Mass/Capacity (6th six weeks)
3.15A The student is expected to explain and record observations using objects, words, pictures, numbers, and technology.	Semantics	Unit 1 – Place Value (1st six weeks) Unit 2 – Addition & Subtraction (1st six weeks) Unit 3 – Money (1st six weeks) Unit 5 – Time & Temperature (2nd six weeks) Unit 6 – Patterns (2nd six weeks) Unit 7 – Multiplication (3rd six weeks) Unit 8 – Division (3rd six weeks) Unit 9 – Graphs (4th six weeks) Unit 11 – Fractions (4th six weeks) Unit 12 – Congruence/Symmetry (4th six weeks) Unit 13 – Geometry (4th six weeks)
3.15B The student is expected to relate informal language to mathematical language and symbols.	Syntax, Semantics	
3.16B The student is expected to justify why an answer is reasonable and explain the solution process.	Pragmatics, Semantics	Units 3, 4, 6, 11, 15

Grade 4 Science
Taken from Texas Essential Knowledge and Skills (TEKS)

State Standard	Communication Skill	District Scope and Sequence
4.2A	The student is expected to plan and implement descriptive investigations, including asking well-defined questions, formulating testable hypotheses, and selecting and using equipment and technology.	Semantics, Syntax	TEKS 4.2 – process skills that are introduced the first week and used all year Unit 1 – Procedures, Lab Safety, & Notebooking (1st six weeks and all year)
4.2D	The student uses scientific inquiry methods during field and laboratory investigations and is expected to communicate valid conclusions.	Semantics, Syntax, Pragmatics	
4.5B	The student is expected to predict and draw conclusions about what happens when part of a system is removed.	Semantics	Unit 4 – Systems, Force and Energy (2nd six weeks)
4.7B	The student is expected to conduct tests, compare data, and draw conclusions about physical properties of matter, including states of matter, conduction, density, and buoyancy.	Semantics	Unit 2 – Properties of Matter (1st six weeks)
4.11B	The student is expected to summarize the effects of the oceans on land.	Semantics	Unit 5 – Changes Over Time (3rd six weeks)

Grade 5 Social Studies
Taken from Texas Essential Knowledge and Skills (TEKS)

	State Standard	Communication Skill	District Scope and Sequence
5.26	The student is expected to communicate in written, oral, and visual forms.	Semantics, Syntax, Pragmatics, Articulation	These social studies TEKS recur throughout the year in all units of study.
5.26A	The student is expected to use social studies terminology correctly.	Semantics	Unit 1 – Thinking About America
5.26B	The student is expected to incorporate main and supporting ideas in verbal and written communication.	Semantics, Syntax	Unit 2 – Living on American Soil Unit 3 – The American Revolution Unit 4 – The United States Constitution
5.26C	The student is expected to express ideas orally based in research and experiences.	Pragmatics, Semantics, Syntax, Articulation	Unit 5 – Growth of a New Nation
5.26D	The student is expected to create written and visual materials, such as journal entries, reports, graphic organizers, outlines, and bibliographies.	Syntax, Semantics	Unit 6 – The Civil War Unit 7 – Expansion and Change Unit 8 – The 20th/21st Century
5.26E	The student is expected to use standard grammar, spelling, sentence structure, and punctuation.	Syntax, Morphology, Semantics	

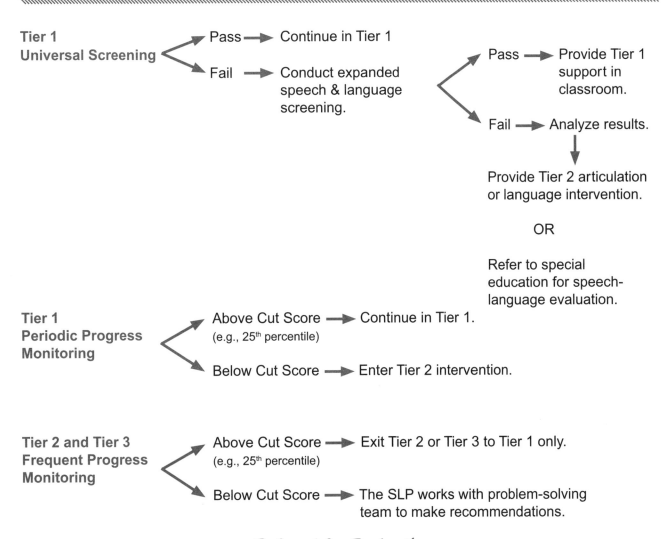

Referral for Evaluation

Decision Variables	Referral Warranted
Student's Learning Profile	Below grade-level speech and language skills AND Student struggles with articulation, phonology, phonemic awareness, vocabulary comprehension, reading comprehension, or pragmatics
Progress in Tier 2 or Tier 3	Little or no progress in speech or language skills following 15 hours of Tier 2 or Tier 3 targeted intervention OR Little or no progress in language-based reading skills following 15 hours of Tier 2 or Tier 3 reading intervention

Week #1		Monday	Tuesday	Wednesday	Thursday	Friday
	8:00	Tier 2 Diagnostic	Tier 2 Diagnostic	Tier 2 Diagnostic	Tier 2 Diagnostic	
	8:30				Tier 1 Observe	
	9:00					
	9:30					
	10:00					Direct Test
	10:30					Direct Test
	11:00		Team Meeting			Direct Test
	11:30		Team Meeting			
	12:00					
	12:30	Direct Test				
	1:00	Direct Test				
	1:30	Direct Test				
	2:00		Tier 3 Observe			Tier 3 Observe
	2:30					
	3:00					
	3:30	Tier 2 Observe		Tier 2 Observe		
	4:00	Progress Data				Progress Data

Week #2		Monday	Tuesday	Wednesday	Thursday	Friday
	8:00	Tier 2 Diagnostic	Tier 2 Diagnostic	Tier 2 Diagnostic	Tier 2 Diagnostic	Tier 3 Observe
	8:30	Tier 2 Observe	Tier 2 Observe		Tier 1 Observe	Direct Test
	9:00					Direct Test
	9:30					Direct Test
	10:00					
	10:30					
	11:00		Team Meeting			
	11:30		Team Meeting			
	12:00					
	12:30		Direct Test			
	1:00		Direct Test			
	1:30		Direct Test			
	2:00					
	2:30					
	3:00					
	3:30	Tier 3 Observe				
	4:00	Progress Data				Progress Data

112

Week #3

	Monday	Tuesday	Wednesday	Thursday	Friday
8:00	Tier 2 Diagnostic	Tier 2 Diagnostic	Tier 2 Diagnostic	Tier 2 Diagnostic	
8:30				Tier 1 Observe	
9:00					
9:30					
10:00					Direct Test
10:30					Direct Test
11:00		Team Meeting			Direct Test
11:30		Team Meeting			
12:00		Tier 3 Observe			
12:30	Direct Test				
1:00	Direct Test				
1:30	Direct Test				
2:00			Tier 2 Observe	Tier 3 Observe	Tier 2 Observe
2:30					
3:00					
3:30					
4:00	Progress Data				Progress Data

Week #4

	Monday	Tuesday	Wednesday	Thursday	Friday
8:00	Tier 2 Diagnostic	Tier 2 Diagnostic	Tier 2 Diagnostic	Tier 2 Diagnostic	Tier 2 Observe
8:30				Tier 1 Observe	Tier 3 Observe
9:00					
9:30					
10:00					
10:30	Tier 3 Observe	Tier 2 Observe			
11:00		Team Meeting			
11:30		Team Meeting			
12:00					
12:30		Direct Test			Direct Test
1:00		Direct Test			Direct Test
1:30		Direct Test			Direct Test
2:00					
2:30					
3:00					
3:30					
4:00	Progress Data				Progress Data

Note: Evaluation activities total about 20 to 25 percent of each work week.

Appendix E1: Screening Tests Analysis Worksheet

Screening Test	Areas Screened	Sensitive	Specific	Easy to Administer & Score	Short	Comments

Appendix E2: Screening Tests Analysis Worksheet Sample

Screening Test	Areas Screened	Sensitive	Specific	Easy to Administer & Score	Short	Comments
Slosson Oral Reading Test	Word calling and word recognition Gives a reading level	Not sure*	Yes	Yes	Yes 3-5 min.	Normed preschool-adult Good reliability and validity Co-normed with Slosson Intelligence Test *Need to match test words with grade-level vocabulary

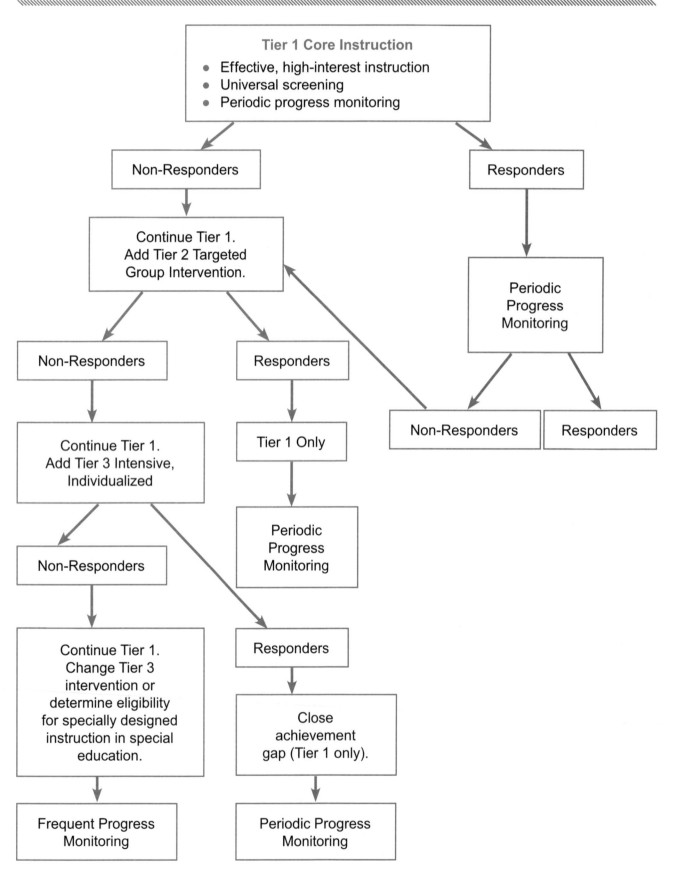

Appendix G: Progress-Monitoring Plan

Student _____ Teacher _____ Grade _____

Tier 1 Curriculum-Based Assessment Results

Date _____ Score _____ Percentile _____

Date _____ Score _____ Percentile _____

Date _____ Score _____ Percentile _____

Tier 2 Intervention Plan Summary

Entry Date _____ Target Skill/Behavior _____

Intervention Approach _____

Progress-Monitoring Method ☐ Included with program ☐ Other _____

Frequency of Intervention	Progress	Date

Intervention Status

☐ Problem resolved; exit Tier 2.

☐ Problem not resolved; redesign or modify Tier 2 intervention.

☐ Problem not resolved; provide more intensity in Tier 3.

☐ Problem not resolved; request referral for special education evaluation.

_____   _____   _____   _____
Principal/Designee   Date   Tier 2 Service Provider   Date
RTI Problem-Solving Team

Appendix H: RTI Problem-Solving Crosswalk

Data-Driven Decisions

Problem-Solving Step	Question	Assessment Procedure	Instruction/ Intervention	Referral for Special Education Evaluation	Specially Designed Instruction
Identify Problem	Does a problem exist? Is the student struggling to meet grade-level expectations?	Universal screening; Periodic progress monitoring	Identify the curriculum areas/skills of concern.	Complete special education referral when an obvious/significant disability exists.	Not applicable
Define Problem	Is there a significant difference between expected and actual performance?	Measure/quantify student performance using curriculum-based assessment; Depict in a chart or graph format.	Specify challenging areas in curriculum based on student's performance on assessments.	Conduct individual comprehensive evaluation; Use RTI to make decisions; Identify disability condition/s.	Review interventions already attempted in order to design customized services.
Design Intervention	What data is there to guide selection of an intervention program/ approach?	Not applicable	Plan instruction/ intervention to meet student needs.	Determine if there is an adverse effect on academic achievement or functional performance resulting from the disability.	IEP Team determines specially designed instruction to meet student needs.
Implement Intervention	Is intervention provided with efficacy and fidelity?	Conduct frequent progress monitoring of target skill/behavior.	Provide Tier 2 or Tier 3 intervention to support classroom instruction.	Not applicable	Provide IEP services when Tier 2 or 3 are not of sufficient frequency, intensity, or duration to meet needs.
Evaluate Response to Intervention	Is the intervention working? Is the problem solved?	Compare performance to individual goal and to grade-level expectations.	Change or stop Tier 2 or Tier 3 when there is little or no progress.	IEP Team determines if specially designed instruction might help student make progress in the general curriculum.	Very frequent progress monitoring of target skill/behavior in IEP

Step 1. Clarify or define systematic RTI progress monitoring in your school or district.

> **Purpose:** Efficient method to evaluate the effectiveness of instruction and intervention and to make changes when needed

> **Rationale**
> 1. Progress monitoring is a systematic way to determine the success of students' response to intervention.
> 2. Progress monitoring emphasizes improved outcomes for students.
> 3. Decisions can be made based on a pattern of performance (individual or group) rather than on one or two pieces of information.

> **Use of Data**
> 1. Collect direct and frequent measures of student progress.
> 2. Use data to establish individual goals for students in need.
> 3. Use data to make instructional change decisions.

Step 2. Identify classrooms or grades to measure. Determine the curriculum area or skills to measure and the frequency schedule for progress monitoring.

Example:

Tier 1

Curriculum Area/ Skills	Grades	Specific Probes	Frequency Schedule
Reading	2 - 5	Accuracy Fluency	Universal screening at beginning of year; three benchmark assessments
Math	2 - 5	Accuracy Understanding	Universal screening at beginning of year; three benchmark assessments
Oral Language/Early Literacy	1 - 3	Grammar System Listening Story Re-Tell	Universal screening at beginning of year; three benchmark assessments
Articulation/ Phonology	1 - 3	Accuracy for age-expected phonemes	Universal screening at beginning of year

Step 3. Develop or acquire the probes. If developing probes, use materials or skills that the students are expected to know by the end of the year. Consistency of administration is important. Plan to administer the same probes in the same order for each progress-monitoring event.

Step 4. Administer the universal screening. Use a frequency distribution chart and a rank order chart of scores to calculate median score and percentiles (See figures 2 and 3, pages 42-43). Use the median score as the baseline data point. Use the percentile ranks and capacity to provide intervention to develop cut scores. At some schools, the cut score may be at the 10th percentile; at other schools, the cut score may be at the 20th or 25th percentile.

Step 5. Rank students within each class screened and determine which students scored below the cut score. Set year-end goals for each student. Start Tier 1 classroom support and/or Tier 2 intervention.

Step 6. Set data collection schedules. Tier 1 periodic progress monitoring is scheduled three times per year. Tier 2 and Tier 3 progress monitoring of the target skill is more frequent and should be scheduled using a systematic set of rules (e.g., data collected every third Monday for Tier 2 and every Monday for Tier 3).

Step 7. Set a year-end goal for each student identified for Tier 2 or Tier 3 intervention. Summarize data in a visual display format (chart or graph) to let students and teachers see the effects of the intervention. The line between the baseline point (median score from the universal screening) and the end of the year goal is the class goal line. The student's score from the universal screening to the end of the year goal is the student's individual goal line. Use results from frequent progress monitoring of the target skill or behavior in Tier 2 or Tier 3 to chart the student's progress and compare progress to the goal line.

Step 8. Use data decision rules to determine when the intervention is working.
   • If three or four consecutive data points are below the individual goal line, change the intervention.
   • If four or five consecutive data points are above the individual goal line, the goal is too low and needs to be increased. When a student scores consistently above the cut score, s/he exits Tier 2 or Tier 3 intervention.
   • If the data points generally follow the individual goal line, continue the intervention.

Student _____ Teacher _____ Grade _____

Universal Screening Results _____

Tier 1 Support   Date Initiated _____

Target Skill/Behavior _____

Instructional Support _____

Review of
Progress Monitoring

		Problem Resolved	Making Progress; Continue.	Below Cut Score; Initiate Tier 2.
Date _____	Percentile _____	☐	☐	☐
Date _____	Percentile _____	☐	☐	☐
Date _____	Percentile _____	☐	☐	☐

Tier 2 Intervention   Date Initiated _____

Target Skill/Behavior _____

Research-Based Intervention _____

Review of Progress Monitoring

		Problem Resolved; Exit Tier 2.	Making Progress; Continue.	Resistant to Intervention; Change Tier 2.	Below Cut Score & Slow Rate of Progress; Initiate Tier 3.
Date _____	Percentile _____	☐	☐	☐	☐
Date _____	Percentile _____	☐	☐	☐	☐
Date _____	Percentile _____	☐	☐	☐	☐
Date _____	Percentile _____	☐	☐	☐	☐
Date _____	Percentile _____	☐	☐	☐	☐
Date _____	Percentile _____	☐	☐	☐	☐

Tier 3 Intervention

Date Initiated _____

Target Skill/Behavior _____

Research-Based Intervention _____

Review of Progress Monitoring

		Problem Resolved; Exit Tier 3.	Making Progress; Continue in Tier 2.	Resistant to Tier 3; Redesign or Change Tier 3.	Making Progress; Intensive Resources Needed to Maintain; Refer to IEP Team.	Below Cut Score & Slow Rate of Progress; Refer to IEP Team.
Date _____	Percentile _____	☐	☐	☐	☐	☐
Date _____	Percentile _____	☐	☐	☐	☐	☐
Date _____	Percentile _____	☐	☐	☐	☐	☐
Date _____	Percentile _____	☐	☐	☐	☐	☐
Date _____	Percentile _____	☐	☐	☐	☐	☐
Date _____	Percentile _____	☐	☐	☐	☐	☐
Date _____	Percentile _____	☐	☐	☐	☐	☐
Date _____	Percentile _____	☐	☐	☐	☐	☐
Date _____	Percentile _____	☐	☐	☐	☐	☐
Date _____	Percentile _____	☐	☐	☐	☐	☐

RTI Problem-Solving Team Members _____

_____

_____

Intervention was provided as described.

_____   _____
Team Leader   Date

Grade _____   Subject _____   Progress-Monitoring Date _____

	Total for Grade								
Class Enrollment									
Range of Raw Scores									
Number Below Cut Score									
Percent Below Cut Score									

Pattern Analysis

☐ More than 20 percent of students in various classrooms scored below cut score. Request curriculum review from central office or curriculum and instruction department.

☐ More than 20 percent of students in one or two classes scored below cut score. Refer to campus administrator for review of teacher's instructional delivery.

☐ Less than 20 percent of students in grade level scored below cut score. Complete Individual Student Review for these students.

_____   _____
Problem-Solving Team Leader   Date of Team Meeting

Grade __1__   Subject __Reading__   Progress-Monitoring Date __9/14__

	Total for Grade	Caudell	Dietz	Chen	Quinones	Teal			
Class Enrollment	90	22	17	17	17	17			
Range of Raw Scores	1-20	1-17	2-16	3-17	2-20	3-16			
Number Below Cut Score	16	5	3	4	2	2			
Percent Below Cut Score	18%	23%	18%	24%	12%	12%			

Pattern Analysis

☐ More than 20 percent of students in various classrooms scored below cut score. Request curriculum review from central office or curriculum and instruction department.

☑ More than 20 percent of students in one or two classes scored below cut score. Refer to campus administrator for review of teacher's instructional delivery.

☑ Less than 20 percent of students in grade level scored below cut score. Complete Individual Student Review for these students.

__Dora Marón__	__9/14__
Problem-Solving Team Leader	Date of Team Meeting

The Source for RTI
Copyright © 2008 LinguiSystems, Inc.

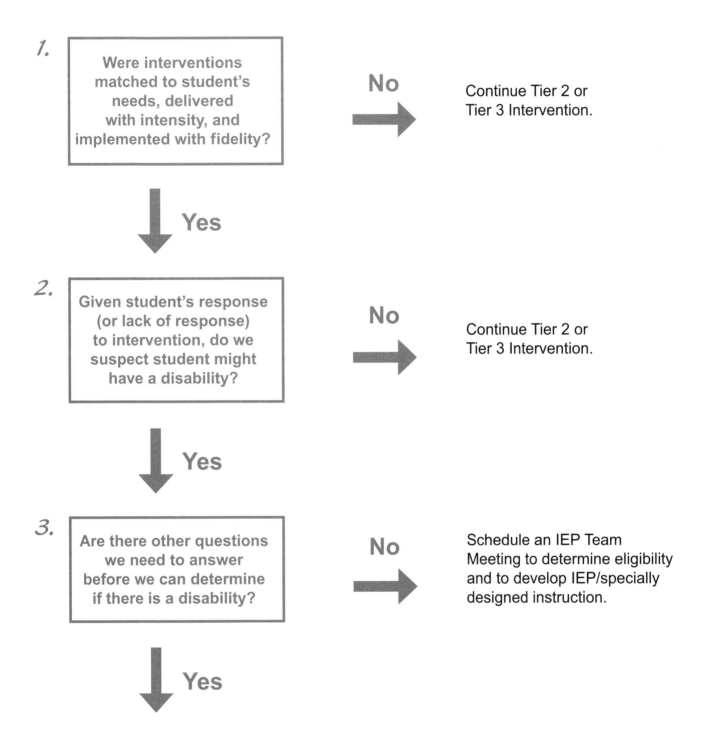

1. Were interventions matched to student's needs, delivered with intensity, and implemented with fidelity?

   No → Continue Tier 2 or Tier 3 Intervention.

   Yes ↓

2. Given student's response (or lack of response) to intervention, do we suspect student might have a disability?

   No → Continue Tier 2 or Tier 3 Intervention.

   Yes ↓

3. Are there other questions we need to answer before we can determine if there is a disability?

   No → Schedule an IEP Team Meeting to determine eligibility and to develop IEP/specially designed instruction.

   Yes ↓

Complete a Comprehensive Individual Evaluation.

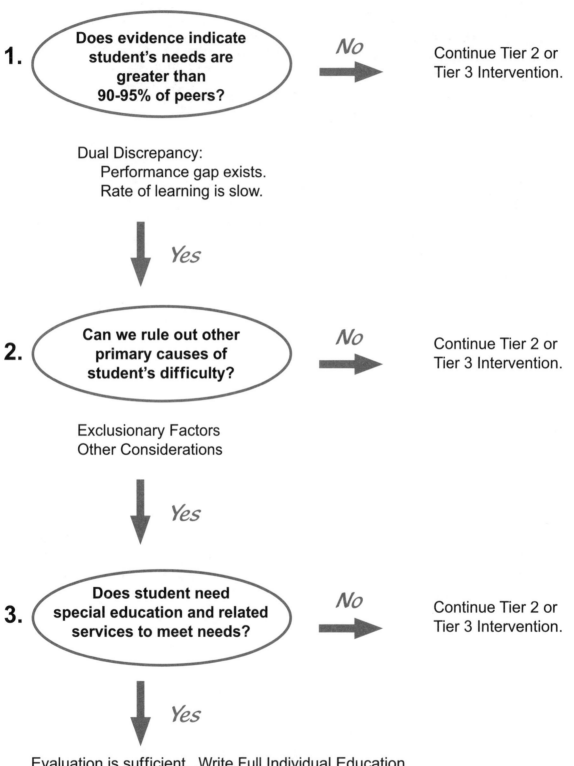

1. Does evidence indicate student's needs are greater than 90-95% of peers? — *No* → Continue Tier 2 or Tier 3 Intervention.

Dual Discrepancy:
   Performance gap exists.
   Rate of learning is slow.

Yes

2. Can we rule out other primary causes of student's difficulty? — *No* → Continue Tier 2 or Tier 3 Intervention.

Exclusionary Factors
Other Considerations

Yes

3. Does student need special education and related services to meet needs? — *No* → Continue Tier 2 or Tier 3 Intervention.

Yes

Evaluation is sufficient. Write Full Individual Education (FIE) Report; IEP Team meets to consider LD eligibility and develop IEP/specially designed instruction.

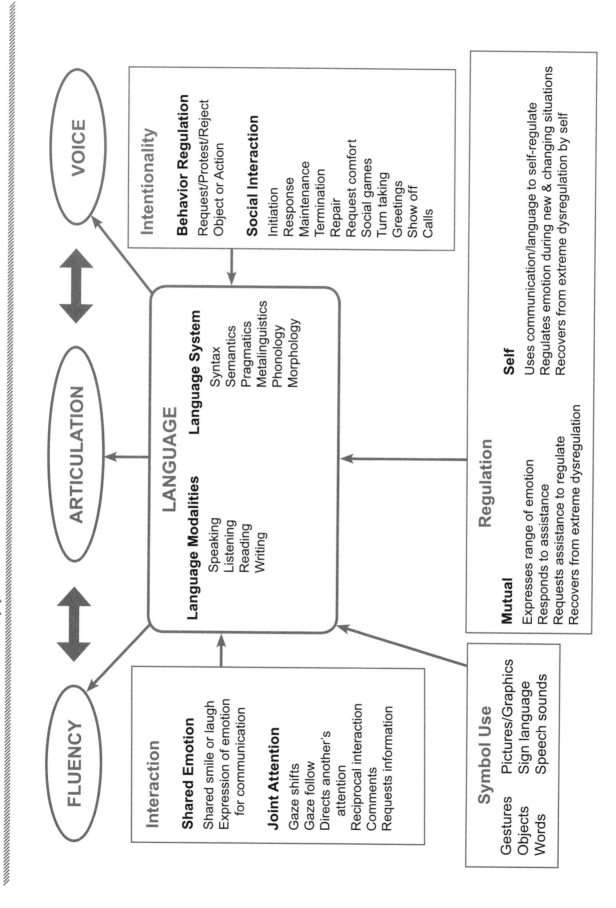

VOICE

ARTICULATION

FLUENCY

Intentionality

Behavior Regulation
Request/Protest/Reject
Object or Action

Social Interaction
Initiation
Response
Maintenance
Termination
Repair
Request comfort
Social games
Turn taking
Greetings
Show off
Calls

LANGUAGE

Language Modalities
Speaking
Listening
Reading
Writing

Language System
Syntax
Semantics
Pragmatics
Metalinguistics
Phonology
Morphology

Interaction

Shared Emotion
Shared smile or laugh
Expression of emotion
for communication

Joint Attention
Gaze shifts
Gaze follow
Directs another's
attention
Reciprocal interaction
Comments
Requests information

Symbol Use
Gestures   Pictures/Graphics
Objects   Sign language
Words   Speech sounds

Regulation

Mutual
Expresses range of emotion
Responds to assistance
Requests assistance to regulate
Recovers from extreme dysregulation

Self
Uses communication/language to self-regulate
Regulates emotion during new & changing situations
Recovers from extreme dysregulation by self

* DATE CONSENT RECEIVED
BY GENERAL EDUCATION:

_____

SPECIAL EDUCATION DEPARTMENT

Information from Educational Records

* DATE RECEIVED BY
SPECIAL EDUCATION:

_____

Student _____   Date of Birth _____

School _____   Grade _____   ID # _____

Parent Name _____   Phone _____

I. REFERRAL INFORMATION

Referred by _____   Position _____

After intensive intervention, what areas continue to be a concern? SPECIFIC REASON FOR REFERRAL:
If the student has a suspected significant disability, (e.g. blind, deaf, cerebral palsy) please complete referral
without regard to intervention.

_____

_____

_____

___ ___ Is the student currently enrolled in school?
YES NO   If NO, explain:

___ ___ Has the student been referred for special
YES NO   education services before? If YES, give
          previous referral date:

___ ___ Has the student been retained? If YES,
YES NO   list grade level(s):

___ ___ Has the student been suspended for
YES NO   disciplinary reasons during the current
          school year? If YES, explain:

___ ___ Is the student in a bilingual class?
YES NO

___ ___ Is the student in an ESL program?
YES NO

SAS*/504 Committee Meeting (circle one):

Date of 1ˢᵗ SAS _____   Please list recommended interventions and results of interventions attempted.

_____

_____

Date of 2ⁿᵈ SAS _____   Please describe results of interventions attempted prior to Special
                                   Education referral.

_____

_____

* See Acronym Key on page 133 for acronyms used in this document.

II. LANGUAGE

Home Language Survey

Date _____

What language is spoken in the home? _____

What language is spoken by the child? _____

For a student identified with limited English proficiency, briefly describe the Language Proficiency Assessment Committee's recommendations. (Please be sure to copy all LPAC pages and WMLS compuscore for this referral.)

_____

_____

_____

At present, what language does the student prefer for: speaking? _____

reading? _____

writing? _____

The student's core academic subjects are taught in: _____ English

_____ Spanish

_____ Other language _____

IDEA 2004

Native Language—The term "native language," when used with respect to an individual who has limited English proficiency, means the language normally used by the individual or, in the case of a child, the language normally used by the parents of the child.

III. EDUCATIONAL BACKGROUND

Schooling Outside U.S.   Country (if known) _____   Grade(s) Completed _____

Schooling in U.S.
Circle each grade completed. For each grade level, if possible, indicate all programs that apply
(e.g., *Gen. Ed., Bil. Ed., ESL*)

PK	K	1	2	3	4	5	6	7	8	9	10	11	12
___	___	___	___	___	___	___	___	___	___	___	___	___	___

IDEA 2004

Special Rule for Eligibility Determination—*In making a determination of eligibility under paragraph (4)(A), a child shall not be determined to be a child with a disability if the determinant factor for such determination is—(A) lack of appropriate instruction in reading, including in the essential components of reading instruction (as defined in section 1208(3) of the Elementary and Secondary Education Act of 1965); (B) lack of instruction in math; or (C) limited English proficiency.*

IV. PHYSICAL (MOTOR ABILITIES, HEALTH, VISION, HEARING)

Does the student participate in PE at school? ___ yes ___ no

Can the student access school environment safely? ___ yes ___ no

Compared to other students in class, can the student perform physical activity appropriately? ___ yes ___ no

Compared to other students in class is the student acquiring handwriting skills slower than expected? ___ yes ___ no

Attendance

The student has been absent _____ days out of _____ school days this year to date.

Reasons for student absences _____

_____

Last year's school attendance (number of absences) _____

Compared to last year, this year the student has been absent ___ more ___ less ___ about the same.
If the student's absences have been consistently high from year to year, please provide a copy of attendance records.

Are you aware of any major medical conditions or injuries? ___ yes ___ no If *yes*, please explain.

_____

List all schools/dates previously attended.

_____

_____

Vision/Hearing: Please attach current Vision/Hearing Screening.

V. EMOTIONAL/BEHAVIORAL

What does the student enjoy most about school? _____

What is the student's favorite subject in school? _____ Least favorite? _____

What seems to serve as a motivator for the student? _____

Do you have information regarding the student's behavior last year? ___ yes ___ no If *yes*, how does the behavior this year compare? _____

Is the student currently receiving support from a school counselor? ___ yes ___ no

Is the student currently receiving support from an outside counselor? ___ yes ___ no

Has the student been suspended, been expelled, or experienced other disciplinary action? ___ yes ___ no
If *yes*, please attach a copy of all current discipline records.

VI. SOCIOLOGICAL

Please be sure to include Parent Information Form (signed and dated).

Do you have information about significant changes in the child's environment? ___ yes ___ no If *yes*, please comment.

_____

Has a parent been informed of progress in interventions provided through general education? ___ yes ___ no

Has a parent been informed that this referral is to determine special education eligibility? ___ yes ___ no

Has a parent received a copy of the ARD Guide book? ___ yes ___ no

---

IDEA 2004

Consent for Initial Evaluation—*The agency proposing to conduct an initial evaluation to determine if the child qualifies as a child with a disability as defined in section 602 shall obtain informed consent from the parent of such child before conducting the evaluation. Parental consent for evaluation shall not be construed as consent for placement for receipt of special education and related services.*

IDEA 2004

Over identification and disproportionality—*The State has in effect, consistent with the purposes of this title and with section 618(d), policies and procedures designed to prevent the inappropriate over identification or disproportionate representation by race and ethnicity of children as children with disabilities, including children with disabilities with a particular impairment described in section 602.*

130

VII. INTELLECTUAL/ADAPTIVE BEHAVIOR

Would the student rather watch or participate in activities in class? Give examples. _____

_____

What activity is the student best at in your classroom? _____

What does the student struggle most with in your classroom? _____

What concerns you the most about the student? _____

Compared to other students in your class, does the student appear to have appropriate social skills? _____

VIII. EDUCATIONAL LEARNING COMPETENCIES (ACADEMIC PERFORMANCE)

With regard to the typical instruction provided in the general education setting, has progress been:

_____ slower than classmates?   _____ about the same as classmates?   _____ faster than classmates?

With regard to general education scientifically research-based interventions (Tier 2 or Tier 3) that have been tried, has student progress: _____ accelerated?   _____ not accelerated?

> With a strong emphasis on methods and strategies grounded in scientifically based reading research and use of assessment instruments, including screening and progress-monitoring measures, and by providing ongoing professional development for teachers, the model is aligned with the provisions of the No Child Left Behind Act.

Before a referral can be processed, copies of the following must be attached if available for student's grade level:

Elementary
___ TPRI/ Tejas Lee
___ PASeries/Flynt Cooter
___ AMI
___ ARI
___ DRA (optional)
___ Gates-MacGinitie
___ Terra Nova/Supera
___ TEKS Checks   English Spanish
    ___ Reading   ___   ___
    ___ Math   ___   ___
    ___ Science   ___   ___
    ___ Writing   ___   ___
___ RTPE/TELPAS
___ TAKS (all available)
___ TAKS (copies of last year and current year scores if available)

Secondary
___ ARI
___ AMI
___ TEKS Checks
    ___ Reading
    ___ Math
    ___ Science
    ___ English
    ___ Social Studies
___ TAKS (all available)
___ PASeries/Flynt Cooter

On TEKS Checks, compare the student performance to class average:

Subjects	Lower than	Same as	Better than	Not applicable
Reading				
Math				
Writing/ELA				
Science				
Social Studies				

Current Grades (Circle those subject **area** grades that are significantly impacted by missing assignments.)

SUBJECT	CURRENT GRADE	ON GRADE LEVEL TEKS		SUBJECT	CURRENT GRADE	ON GRADE LEVEL TEKS	
		☐ YES	☐ NO			☐ YES	☐ NO
		☐ YES	☐ NO			☐ YES	☐ NO
		☐ YES	☐ NO			☐ YES	☐ NO
		☐ YES	☐ NO			☐ YES	☐ NO
		☐ YES	☐ NO	Conduct grades		☐ YES	☐ NO

This student's grades:

___ have increased each year.
___ have stayed about the same each year.
___ have decreased each year.
___ dropped suddenly in grade _____

Compared with the other students in your class, this student's grades:

___ are better.
___ are about the same.
___ are worse.

IDEA 2004

Determination of Eligibility and Educational Need—Upon completion of the administration of assessments and other evaluation measures, (A) the determination of whether the child is a child with a disability as defined in section 602(3) and the educational needs of the child shall be made by a team of qualified professionals and the parent of the child in accordance with paragraph (5); and (B) a copy of the evaluation report and the documentation of eligibility shall be given to the parent.

IDEA 2004

Specific Learning Disabilities —(B) Additional Authority. In determining whether a child has a specific learning disability, a local educational agency may use a process that determines if the child responds to scientific, research-based intervention as a part of the evaluation procedures described in paragraphs (2) and (3).

SIGNATURE OF PERSON COMPLETING THIS SECTION   **POSITION**   **DATE**

Attachments

☐ Proof of Identification and Age: (please check one)
    ___ Birth certificate
    ___ Passport
    ___ School ID card, records, or report card
    ___ Military ID
    ___ Hospital birth record
    ___ Adoption records
    ___ Church baptismal record
    ___ Any other legal document that establishes identity

☐ Enrollment Card

☐ Home Language Survey, LPAC Pages, and WMLS Compuscore

☐ Health Information

☐ Emergency Care Card

☐ Parent Information Form

☐ Copy of Class Schedule (for secondary only)

☐ Observation of Academic Performance

☐ Information for Classroom Teacher (for secondary core subjects, one from each teacher)

☐ Copy of Notice of FIE

☐ Consent for FIE

☐ Receipt of Procedural Safeguards

☐ Copy of Current Discipline Records (if behavior is noted as a concern in Section V).

Acronym Key

SAS – Student Assistance System; district's name for the campus problem-solving team
LPAC – Language Proficiency Assessment Committee
WMLS – Woodcock-Munoz Language Survey
ESL – English as a Second Language
ARD – Admission Review and Dismissal Committee; Texas name for IEP Team
TPRI – Texas Primary Reading Inventory
Tejas Lee – Spanish companion of TPRI
ARI – Accelerated Reading Initiative
AMI – Accelerated Math Initiative
DRA – Developmental Reading Assessment
TEKS Checks – district developed benchmark tests matched to state standards
RTPE – Reading Test of Proficiency in English
TELPAS – Texas English Language Proficiency Assessment System
TAKS – Texas Assessment of Knowledge and Skills; state assessment system
TEKS – Texas Essential Knowledge and Skills; state curriculum standards
FIE – Full Individual Evaluation

Used with permission from
Irving Independent School District

Appendix P: Multidisciplinary Team Planning Form for Individual Student Evaluation

Student _____ Grade/Age _____ School _____ Teacher _____

MDT Members _____

Date of Referral _____ Date of Initial Team Meeting _____

Referral Information/Concern _____

RTI Data

		Above Cut Score	Below Cut Score
Tier 1 Core Instruction	Universal Screening _____ Date _____	☐ ☐☐☐	☐ ☐☐☐
	Periodic Progress Monitoring _____ Date _____		
	_____ Date _____		
	_____ Date _____		
	Tier 1 Classroom Support Start Date _____ Stop Date _____		
	Describe:		
	☐ Student back on track ☐ Student considered for Tier 2		
Tier 2 Targeted Group Intervention	Start Date _____ Change/Stop Date _____		
	Intervention Approach: _____		
	Intervention Review (from appendix J): _____		
	☐ Resistant to intervention; Changed Tier 2 ☐ Slow/Limited progress (need more information) ☐ Other: _____		
Tier 3 Intensive, Individualized Intervention	Start Date _____ Change/Stop Date _____		
	Intervention Approach: _____		
	Intervention Review (from appendix J): _____		
	☐ Resistant to intervention; Changed Tier 3 ☐ Slow progress (need intensive resources for lengthy duration)		
	☐ Slow/Limited progress (need more information)		

Evaluation Question/s: _____

Area		Address Further	Assess Further	MDT Member Responsible	Tests/Tools/ Strategies	Target Date for Completion
Sociological	☐	☐	☐			
Physical/ Motor/Medical	☐	☐	☐			
Cognitive Development	☐	☐	☐			
Adaptive Behavior	☐	☐	☐			
Educational Performance/ Achievement	☐	☐	☐			
Emotional/ Behavioral	☐	☐	☐			
Assistive Technology	☐	☐	☐			

The Source for RTI

Area		Address Further	Assess Further	MDT Member Responsible	Tests/Tools /Strategies	Target Date for Completion
Articulation	☐	☐	☐			
Voice	☐	☐	☐			
Fluency	☐	☐	☐			
Language System Syntax Semantics Pragmatics Metalinguistics Phonology Morphology Modalities Speaking Listening Reading Writing	☐	☐	☐			
Other Communication Interactions Intentionality Symbol Use Regulation	☐	☐	☐			

Appendix Q: Adverse Effect on Educational Performance

Speech or language impairment means a communication disorder...that adversely affects a child's educational performance [300.8(c) (11)]. In developing each child's IEP, the IEP Team must consider the academic, developmental, and functional needs of the child [300.324(a) (1)]. The IEP...must include a statement of the child's present levels of *academic achievement* and *functional performance* [300.320(a) (1)].

Academic Achievement—generally refers to a child's performance in academic areas (reading or language arts, math, science, history).

No Adverse Effect	Temporary or Episodic Adverse Effect	Significant Adverse Effect
Student's communication disorder—such as stuttering, impaired articulation, language impairment, voice impairment—has no adverse affect on academic performance or achievement.	Data about the student's learning profile indicates that the student has a communication disorder and that any adverse effect on academic achievement is likely to be short term, temporary, or episodic.	There is a direct, noticeable relationship between the student's communication disorder and academic performance or achievement.
Student's response to Tier 2 or Tier 3 intervention indicates that communicative competence is at a level to allow for expected progress in meeting grade-level standards without special education or related services.	Student's rate of learning, motivation, and responsiveness to intervention are positive indicators.	The student has not responded to Tier 2 or Tier 3 interventions with expected performance of target skill or rate of learning.
Student's communication skills are proportionate with overall functioning level.	Data indicates that the student's educational performance in the curriculum will likely require specially designed instruction from the SLP.	The student's communication disorder contributes to academic struggle or below expected achievement.
		The student's communication disorder is out of proportion with overall functioning level.

Sample Rubric Only
Should be customized for eligibility guidelines, state curriculum standards, and shared understanding of "academic achievement and functional performance"

Functional Performance—generally refers to skills or activities that are not academic or related to a child's academic achievement; often used in the context of routine activities of everyday living.

No Adverse Effect	Temporary or Episodic Adverse Effect	Significant Adverse Effect
Student's communication disorder has no adverse effect on functional performance in academic or nonacademic settings or extra-curricular activities.	Data about the student's learning profile indicates that the student has a communication disorder and that any adverse effect on functional performance is likely to be short term, temporary, or episodic.	Communication skills limit participation in self-care, interpersonal, and daily routines.
Student's response to Tier 2 or Tier 3 intervention indicates that communicative competence is at a level to allow for expected progress for grade level.	Student's rate of learning, motivation, and responsiveness to intervention are positive indicators.	The student has no functional communication, has limited means of expression, or the social/emotional adjustment is affected by the communication disorder.
Student's communication skills are proportionate with overall adaptive functioning level.	Data indicates that the student's communication during activities of daily living will likely require specially designed instruction from the SLP.	Communication patterns are noticeably disrupted and interfere with interaction and functional performance.
		The student's communication disorder is out of proportion with overall intellectual and adaptive functioning level.

Sample Rubric Only
Should be customized for eligibility guidelines, state curriculum standards, and shared understanding of "academic achievement and functional performance"

Appendix R: Language-Based Reading Skills Rubric
(Teacher Rating)

Use this rubric to rate language-based reading skills for students scoring below the cut score on the universal screening of reading or periodic progress-monitoring assessments.

1	2	3	4	5
Poor vocabulary	Below grade-level vocabulary (both key words and content specific words)	Use of vague rather than specific vocabulary ("thing," "stuff," "do," "it")	At grade level for basic vocabulary; Needs to improve content vocabulary	Good vocabulary
Difficulty answering low-level questions ("what, when, where")	Difficulty answering "how" and "why" questions	Provides incomplete answers to questions	Answers questions but does not expand or extend topic; Does not ask higher level questions	Asks and answers questions well and provides details
Poor word awareness	Emerging word and syllable awareness	Below grade-level phoneme, syllable, and word awareness	Developing good phoneme, syllable, and word awareness	At grade level for phoneme, syllable, and word awareness
Difficulty with rhyming and breaking words into syllables	Can follow simple two-part instructions	Does not have good listening attention	Developing good listening behaviors; Needs reminders	Good listener for a variety of purposes
Does not seem to understand or follow classroom instructions	Low verbal skills for grade	Difficulty carrying on a conversation	Participates in conversations	Conversation and discourse skills are well developed
Does not express ideas clearly	Speaks like a younger child (manner and content)	Immature grammar system	Grammar skills at grade level	Strong oral and written grammar system
Speaks in short phrases or incomplete sentences				

Student Name/Score

Return to _____

Grade Level _____

Content Area ☐ Reading ☐ Language Arts ☐ Social Studies ☐ Math ☐ Science

Curriculum Unit/Target Skills

_____

_____

Language Modality	Student Expectations	Barriers to Learning	Student Support Activities
Listening			
Speaking			
Reading			
Writing			

Appendix S2: Language Demands of the Curriculum Analysis Worksheet Sample

Grade Level 2

Content Area ☐ Reading ☑ Language Arts ☑ Social Studies ☐ Math ☐ Science

Curriculum Unit/Target Skills

Unit: Fiction Folktales "Arthur Writes a Story"

Social Studies: Trade and barter; Increase vocabulary—economic terms

Language Modality	Student Expectations	Barriers to Learning	Student Support Activities
Listening	Listen to get information to solve problems, to enjoy and appreciate; connect experiences and ideas through listening	Poor attention for listening; no strategies for listening	Independent listening station for a variety of purposes; discuss ways to be a better listener
Speaking	Participate in oral language experiences; communicate clearly for different purposes	Little experience speaking for different purposes	Model using analytical and evaluative statements; discuss polite interaction and social conventions at school
Reading	Recognize character, setting, plot in selected texts; use prefixes and compound words for word identification	Little experience with stories; poorly developed metalinguistic awareness	Multiple teacher Read-Alouds – stories with strong structure; word awareness activities
Writing	Compose explanatory writing; combine sentences; use of action verbs; verb-tense, use of "have"	No background knowledge to support writing topic	Pre-writing using graphic organizers; writing based on experiential learning; Wordwall section: connecting words

Appendix T1: Language Demands of the Curriculum
Teacher Observation

Name _____ Grade _____ Subject _____ Date _____

Topic of Lesson _____

Student Expectations_____

Language Objectives (see Analysis Worksheet) _____

Student Activities	Student's Response
Grouping ☐ Whole Class ☐ Small Group ☐ Partners ☐ Independent	**Engagement:**
Language Modalities ☐ Listening ☐ Speaking ☐ Reading ☐ Writing	**Note Strengths/Weaknesses:**
Scaffolding ☐ Modeling ☐ Guided ☐ Student Collaboration ☐ Independent	**Amount of Structure Needed to Support Learning:**
Strategies ☐ Hands-on ☐ Technology ☐ Experiential ☐ Constructivist ☐ Peer Interaction ☐ Lecture	**Interest in Lesson:**
Assessment ☐ Written ☐ Oral ☐ Portfolio ☐ Project Based ☐ Group ☐ Individual	**Confidence Demonstrating Learning:**

Appendix T2: Language Demands of the Curriculum
Teacher Observation Sample

Name _Joseph_   Grade _2_   Subject _Language Arts_   Date _11/30_

Topic of Lesson _Choosing a Writing Topic (Arthur Writes a Story)_

Student Expectations _generate a list of "My Ideas" in writing journal_

Language Objectives (see Analysis Worksheet) _participate in class discussion, interact verbally with partner_

Student Activities	Student's Response
Grouping ☑ Whole Class ☐ Small Group ☑ Partners ☐ Independent	**Engagement:** higher engagement during partner activity than whole class activity
Language Modalities ☑ Listening ☑ Speaking ☐ Reading ☑ Writing	**Note Strengths/Weaknesses:** difficulty attending during whole class discussion
Scaffolding ☑ Modeling ☑ Guided ☑ Student Collaboration ☐ Independent	**Amount of Structure Needed to Support Learning:** seems to do better with something in his hands and with visual support
Strategies ☐ Hands-on ☐ Technology ☐ Experiential ☐ Constructivist ☑ Peer Interaction ☐ Lecture	**Interest in Lesson:** enjoyed working with partner **Confidence Demonstrating Learning:** needed teacher guidance to get his ideas into his journal
Assessment ☐ Written ☐ Oral ☐ Portfolio ☐ Project Based ☐ Group ☑ Individual - Journal	

Name _____ Grade _____ Subject _____ Date _____

Topic of Lesson _____

Activities Observed _____

Note the student's response during instruction: (1) areas of strength and high engagement where learning is facilitated and (2) areas of struggle, disconnect, or where student may be falling behind.

	Listening	Speaking	Reading	Writing
Key Vocabulary				
Content Vocabulary				
Background Knowledge				
Comprehension				
Linguistic Complexity				
Questioning				
Metalinguistic Abilities				
Conversation/ Discourse/ Narrative				

The Source for RTI
Copyright © 2008 LinguiSystems, Inc.

Appendix U2: Language Demands of the Curriculum
SLP Observation Sample

Name <u>Joseph</u>　　　　Grade <u>2</u>　　Subject <u>Language Arts</u>　　Date <u>11/30</u>

Topic of Lesson <u>Expository Writing</u>

Activities Observed <u>Using graphic organizers to display expository pattern of text</u>

Note the student's response during instruction: (1) areas of strength and high engagement where learning is facilitated and (2) areas of struggle, disconnect, or where student may be falling behind.

	Listening	Speaking	Reading	Writing
Key Vocabulary	better attention when auditory paired with visual	good basic vocabulary		
Content Vocabulary		developing vocabulary; needs work		
Background Knowledge			needs overt connections between past learning and text; weak	difficulty connecting thoughts
Comprehension	seems to under-stand instructions			
Linguistic Complexity		immature grammar		
Questioning				prefers to draw pictures than write sentences
Metalinguistic Abilities		poor use of morphological information to remember words	poor decoding	
Conversation/ Discourse/ Narrative		reluctant to participate in class discussion		

Name _____   Date _____

Target Sound _____   Words of the Week

1. _____   6. _____

2. _____   7. _____

3. _____   8. _____

4. _____   9. _____

5. _____   10. _____

Say your list of words three times to three people every day this week. Write the number of times you pronounced the words correctly in each box.

	#1	#2	#3
Monday			
Tuesday			
Wednesday			
Thursday			
Friday			
Saturday			
Sunday			

_____   _____
Parent/Guardian   Student

Return your signed practice record to _____ on Monday.

Appendix W: Accelerated Reading Framework
Elliott Elementary School

Goal

To accelerate teaching and learning for students with disabilities to ensure success toward grade-level reading skills. Students with disabilities benefit from instruction in the general education setting in addition to specially designed special education instruction.

Rationale

Children with better reading skills have fewer behavior problems in school (Fleming et al. 2004). Traditional resource room settings do not appear to have a significant effect on reading skills (Bentum & Aaron 2003). Children need more intense, explicit, and systematic delivery services in a small group with consistent monitoring (Torgeson et al. 2001; Fletcher 2006).

Purpose

The framework provides reading instruction through a combination of general education curriculum, tutoring support through the Texas Accelerated Reading Initiative, and specially designed reading instruction for students with disabilities. This specially designed reading program is in addition to state designated reading time for a student's grade level. Students receive one hour a day of supplemental reading instruction.

Program Design

- The program is designed for students with disabilities.
- The schedule consists of two, thirty-minute reading periods per day, five days a week (in addition to classroom instruction and Tier 1 classroom support).
- Instructional materials are selected based on appropriate instruction for the specific area of reading the student is working on. For example, Read Naturally is appropriate to work on reading fluency, but not reading comprehension.
- Student groups are no larger than four students per special education teacher.
- Student groups are short term and fluid based on frequent progress monitoring and student mastery.
- Reading groups are designed so that each teacher specializes in one area of reading (NRP 2000). Instruction focuses on a specific area of reading based on student need and based on the balanced literacy approach used in the general education classroom:
  Phonemic Awareness
  Phonics
  Vocabulary
  Comprehension
  Reading Fluency
- Benchmark data is used for initial placement based on a teacher-made, curriculum-based assessment.
- Progress monitoring is completed every two to three weeks to adjust instruction and to check student progress.

Program Results

Based on state assessments, special education students in third through fifth grade who took part in the program made more than one year of progress in reading during the school year. Students with disabilities who participated in the program made significantly more progress than students with disabilities who did not receive the intervention. Students who participated in the program also made more progress than they had made the year prior to the program.

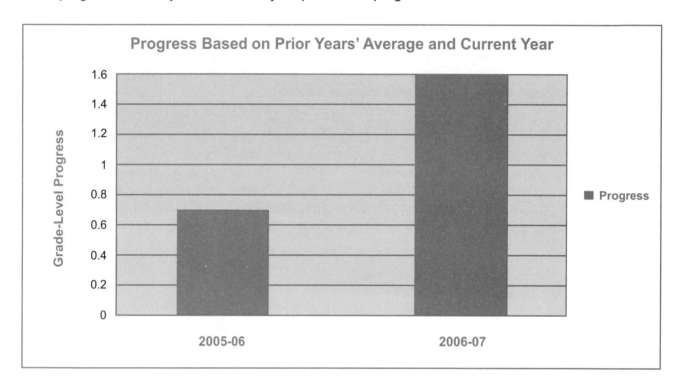

Success Stories

Kaitlin

In 2002, Kaitlin enrolled in kindergarten at Elliott Elementary. She was only able to attend school half days due to her aggressive, out-of-control behavior. Reading was a huge struggle. As the years progressed, Kaitlin received more and more pull-out time in the special education setting. Success was limited.

With much hesitation, Kaitlin was recommended for the Accelerated Reading Class by her special education teacher. She returned to the general education classroom for Tier 1 and Tier 2 instruction and received Tier 3 special education reading support. A system of student progress charting was put into effect. Kaitlin began with sight words and moved to decoding, fluency, and comprehension. With each step, she charted her progress. As her reading confidence and levels changed, so did her behavior. A successful fifth grader, Kaitlin is now reading close to grade level with great success. Her behavior is exceptional and she has even become a mentor for younger students in the special education setting.

Kaitlin's mom is very proud of her daughter and loves the progress charts she receives at home on a regular basis.

Eli

As a second grader at Elliott Elementary, Eli was referred to special education due to his lack of progress in reading and writing. Classroom accommodations had not been successful. In third grade, Eli began a special education reading program. His progress was minimal.

Mid-year in third grade, the special education teacher recommended Eli for the Accelerated Reading Class. He began at a K-1 reading level and started in the sight words and decoding components of the program. In less than a year, he had moved to the fluency and comprehension components of the program. Eli was very excited and proud to see his progress charted. In 2007-08, as a fifth grader, he returned to the general education classroom, reading at a level of 4.5. Eli received Tier 1 and Tier 2 instruction plus Tier 3 reading support at the beginning of the year. During fifth grade, he had a three-year re-evaluation and no longer qualified for special education.

Testimonials

"Last night, my daughter went to her room and gathered up a big bunch of books. We sat on my bed and she read me about three of them. Oh my gosh!!! Wow!! I'm absolutely blown away! She's drastically improved. I certainly bragged on her – over and over. And I told her how much I could see this new reading program she's doing in the morning and the afternoon has really helped her…and how proud I am of her for sticking with it and giving it a chance to help her. She just grinned. I'm definitely seeing the huge steps she's making…and I couldn't be happier! Thank you so much!!!"

—Parent of a second-grade student at Elliott Elementary

"Hello Everyone!

I wanted to let you know that our student did a great job today in guided reading. He volunteered to read a sentence out loud and he had great ideas for the novel we are reading. He made great predictions and gave an adjective to describe one of the characters! He was on task and he even independently completed a written assignment that went along with the book. I'm so proud of him!! After he left the reading group, I did have to redirect him once, but he was open to someone helping him. He then completed the activity with another student's assistance. Thanks for your support."

—E-mail from general education third-grade teacher to special education teachers at Elliott Elementary

American Speech-Language-Hearing Association. (2006). *Responsiveness-to-intervention professional consultation packet.* http://www.asha.org/members/slp/schools/prof-consult/Rtol.htm

Canter, A. (2006, February). Problem solving and RTI: New roles for school psychologists. *Communique, 34*(5). http://www.nasponline.org/publications/cq/cq345rti.aspx

Center on Instruction. *Special education: Grades K-12.* Go to the "Special Education" menu on the home page to find useful materials, PowerPoint presentations, and papers from multiple sources on RTI. http://www.centeroninstruction.org/index.cfm

Council for Exceptional Children. *Response-to-intervention—The promise and the peril.* http://www.cec.sped.org/AM/Template.cfm?Section=Search&Template=/CM/HTMLDisplay. cfm&ContentID=7600

Ehren, B., Montgomery, J., Rudebusch, J., & Whitmire, K. (2006). *Responsiveness to intervention: New roles for speech-language pathologists.* http://www.asha.org/members/slp/schools/prof-consult/NewRolesSLP.htm

International Reading Association. *Focus on response to intervention: RTI resource library.* http://www.reading.org/resources/issues/focus_rti_library.html

International Reading Association. (2006). *The role of reading instruction in addressing the overrepresentation of minority children in special education in the United States.* www.reading.org/resources/issues/positions_minorities.html

Klotz, M.B., & Canter, A. (2006). *Response to intervention (RTI): A primer for parents.* www.nasponline.org/resources/factsheets/rtiprimer.aspx

Mellard, D. (2004). *Understanding responsiveness to intervention in learning disabilities determination.* www.nrcld.org/about/publications/papers/mellard.html

National Center for Culturally Responsive Educational Systems (NCCRESt). http://www.nccrest.org

National Center for Learning Disabilities. *Responsiveness to intervention and learning disabilities.* http://www.ncld.org/index.php?option=content&task=view&id=497

National Joint Committee on Learning Disabilities. (2005). *Responsiveness to intervention and learning disabilities.* www.ldonline.org/article/11498

National Research Center on Learning Disabilities. *Responsiveness-to-intervention evaluation, technical assistance, and dissemination activities.* This website offers the results of meetings, conferences, and papers, as well as a link to the model site research carried out with the network of Regional Resource Centers (RRCs). www.nrcld.org/topics/rti.html

RTI Resource Center (a clearinghouse for RTI academic research sites, RTI associations, and presentations) **http://www.autoskill.com/intervention/rti.php?gclid=CJyg4mlkCFRF3SAodxTJ-MQ**

School Social Work Association of America. (2006). *Response to intervention: New roles for school social workers.* **http://www.sswaa.org/Role_of_SSW_in_RTI_FINAL_11-06.pdf**

Wrightslaw. *What you need to know about IDEA 2004 response to intervention (RTI): New ways to identify specific learning disabilities.* **www.wrightslaw.com/info/rti.index.htm**

RTI Efforts in Various States

Colorado
http://www.cde.state.co.us/cdesped/Rtl.asp

Minnesota
http://education.state.mn.us/mdeprod/groups/SpecialEd/documents/Announcement/009253.pdf

Nebraska
http://rtinebraska.unl.edu/index.html

New Jersey
http://www.nj.gov/education/bilingual/pd/pp/ell2.htm

New Mexico
Guidance document for New Mexico schools
http://www.ped.state.nm.us/div/acc.assess/assess/dl/misc/RtlManualFinalCombo2006%2012-06.pdf

North Carolina
Problem-Solving Model and Training Materials
http://www.ncpublicschools.org/ec/development/learning/intervention/rtimaterials

Oregon
http://www.ode.state.or.us/initiatives/idea/rti.aspx

Texas
http://www.tea.state.tx.us/special.ed/rti/

Washington
http://www.k12.wa.us/SpecialEd/Rtl.aspx

Wisconsin
http://dpi.wi.gov/sped/rti.html

Adelman, H.S., & Taylor, L. (1998). Reframing mental health in schools and expanding school reform. *Educational Psychologist, 33*(4), 135-152.

American Speech-Language-Hearing Association. (1993). Guidelines for caseload size and speech-language service delivery in the schools. *ASHA*, 35(Suppl.), 33-39. Rockville, MD: Author.

American Speech-Language-Hearing Association. (2002). *A workload approach to caseload standards in schools.* Rockville, MD: Author.

American Speech-Language-Hearing Association. (2003). *Implementation guide: A workload analysis approach to caseload standards in schools.* Rockville, MD: Author.

American Speech-Language-Hearing Association. (2005). *Evidence-based practice in communication disorders* [Position Statement]. Rockville, MD: Author.
http://www.asha.org/docs/html/PS2005-00221.html

American Speech-Language-Hearing Association. (2006). *Responsiveness to intervention: New roles for speech-language pathologists* [Technical Assistance Paper]. Rockville, MD: Author.

American Speech-Language-Hearing Association. (2007). *Directory of speech-language pathology assessment instruments.* Rockille, MD: Author.

American Speech-Language-Hearing Association. (2007). *Implementing IDEA 2004 Part I: Conducting educationally relevant evaluations.* Rockville, MD: Author.

American Speech-Language-Hearing Association. (2007). *Implementing IDEA 2004 Part II. Developing educationally relevant IEPs.* Rockville, MD: Author.

Bentum, E.E., & Aaron, P.G. (2003). Does reading instruction in learning disability resource rooms really work: A longitudinal study. *Reading Psychology, 24*, 361-382.

Berrueta-Clement, J.R., Schweinhart, L.J., Barnett, W.S., Epstein, A.S., & Weikart, D.P. (1984). Changed lives: The effects of the Perry Preschool Program on youths through age 19. *Monographs of the High/Scope Educational Research Foundation*, No. 8. Ypsilanti, MI: High/Scope Press.

Blanchard, K.H., & Johnson, S. (1985). *The one-minute manager.* New York: Harper Collins.

Bocian, K., Beebe, M., MacMillan, D., & Gresham, F.M. (1999). Competing paradigms in learning disabilities classification by schools and variations in the meaning of discrepant achievement. *Learning Disabilities Research & Practice, 14*, 1-14.

Boyd, V. (1992). *School context: Bridge or barrier to change.* Austin, TX: Southwest Educational Development Laboratory.

Bradley, R., Danielson, L., & Hallahan, D. (Eds.). (2002). *Identification of learning disabilities: Research to practice.* Mahwah, NJ: Lawrence Erlbaum Associates.

Butler, K., & Nelson, N. (2005). Responsiveness to intervention and the speech-language pathologist. *Topics in Language Disorders, 25,* 2.

Code of Federal Regulations (CFR). *Assistance to states for the education of children with disabilities and the early intervention program for infants and toddlers with disabilities* [Final regulations]. C.F.R., Title 34 § 300, 301, and 303 (2006).

Deno, S. (1985). Curriculum-based measurement: The emerging alternative. *Exceptional Children, 52,* 219-232.

Deno, S., & Mirkin, P. (1977). *Data-based program modification.* Minneapolis, MN: Leadership Training Institute for Special Education.

Donovan, M.S., & Cross, C.T. (2002). *Minority students in special and gifted education.* Washington DC: National Academy Press.

DuFour, R., DuFour, R., Eaker, R., & Karhanek, G. (2004). *Whatever it takes: How a professional learning community responds when kids don't learn.* Bloomington, IN: National Education Service.

Dunaway, C.L. (2006). *Story talk.* Unpublished manuscript, San Diego Unified School District.

Fleming, C.B., Harachi, T.W., Cortes, R.C., Abbott, R.D., & Catalano, R.F. (2004). Level and change in reading scores and attention problems during elementary school as predictors of problem behavior in middle school. *Journal of Emotional and Behavioral Disorder, 13,* 130-144.

Fletcher, J.M. (2006). *Why RTI? Research and policy foundations.* Paper presented at Texas Special Education Response to Intervention Summit, Austin, TX.

Frey, N., & Fisher, D. (2006). *Language arts workshop: Purposeful reading and writing instruction.* Upper Saddle River, NJ: Pearson Education, Inc.

Fuchs, D., Fuchs, L.S., & Compton, D.L. (2004). Identifying reading disabilities by responsiveness to instruction: Specifying measure and criteria. *Learning Disability Quarterly, 27.*

Fuchs, D., Fuchs, L.S., & Compton, D.L. (2005). *Experimental research studies on responsiveness to intervention (RTI) in reading and math.* **http://www.nrcld.org/rti_practices/research/nrcld.html**

Fuchs, L.S. (2002). Three conceptualizations of "treatment" in a response-to-treatment framework for LD identification. In R. Bradley, L. Danielson, & D. Hallahan (Eds.), *Identification of learning disabilities: Research to practice* (pp. 521-529). Mahwah, NJ: Lawrence Erlbaum Associates.

Fuchs, L.S. (2003). Assessing intervention responsiveness: Conceptual and technical issues. *Learning Disabilities Research and Practice, 18*(3), 172-187.

Fuchs, L.S., & Fuchs, D. (1998). Treatment validity: A unifying concept for reconceptualizing the identification of learning disabilities. *Learning Disabilities Research and Practice, 13*, 204-219.

Fullan, M. (1993). *Dynamics of the change process.* North Central Regional Educational Laboratory. **http://www.ncrel.org/sdrs/areas/issues/educatrs/leadrshp/le5dynam.htm**

Government Office for the South West. (2006). *The change management matrix.* **http://www.oursouthwest.com/SusBus/matrix.pdf**

Gresham, F.M. (2002). Responsiveness to intervention: An alternative approach to the identification of learning disabilities. In R. Bradley, L. Danielson, & D. Hallahan (Eds.), *Identification of learning disabilities: Research to practice* (pp. 467-519). Mahwah, NJ: Lawrence Erlbaum Associates.

Haager, D., Klingner, J., & Vaughn, S. (2007). *Evidence-based reading practices for response to intervention.* Baltimore, MD: Brookes Publishing.

Haerwas, L.B., & Woolman, I.S. (Eds.). (2006). Interim guidance regarding service delivery and learning disability identification: Post-IDEA reauthorization, pending Rhode Island regulation revision (3rd ed.). Providence, RI: Rhode Island Department of Elementary and Secondary Education Document. **www.ritap.org/rti/content/interim%20guidance.pdf**

Hanushek, E.A., Kain, J.F., & Rivkin, S.G. (2002). Inferring program effects for special populations: Does special education raise achievement for students with disabilities? *Review of Economics and Statistics, 84*(4) 584-599.

Hord, S.M. (Ed.). (2004). *Learning together, leading together: Changing schools through professional learning communities.* New York: Teachers College Press.

Howell, K., & Nolet, V. (2000). *Curriculum-based evaluation: Teaching and decision making.* Belmont, CA: Wadsworth.

Ikeda, M., & Gustafsen, J.K. (2002). *Heartland AEA 11's problem solving process impact on issues related to special education.* (Research Report No. 2002-01.) Unpublished manuscript.

Individuals with Disabilities Education Improvement Act (IDEA) Amendments, 20 U.S.C. § 1400 *et seq.* (2004).

Klingner, J.K., & Edwards, P.A. (2006). Cultural considerations with response to intervention models. *Reading Research Quarterly, 41*(1), 108-117.

Lyon, G.R., & Fletcher, J. (2001). Early warning system. *Education Matters, 1*(2), 2-29. **http://www.hoover.org/publications/ednext/3389276.html**

154

Marzano, R.J., Pickering, D.J., & Pollock, J.E. (2001). *Classroom instruction that works: Research-based strategies for increasing student achievement.* Alexandria, VA: Association for Supervision and Curriculum Development.

McCook, J.E. (2006). *The RTI guide: Developing and implementing a model in your schools.* Horsham, PA: LRP Publications.

Mellard, D. (2004). *Understanding responsiveness to intervention in learning disabilities determination.* **www.nrcld.org/about/publications/papers/mellard.html**

Montgomery, J., & Moore-Brown, B. (2005). *START IN: Students are responding to intervention: A response to intervention (RTI) program for reading.* Greenville, SC: Super Duper Publications.

Moore-Brown, B., & Montgomery, J. (2001). *Making a difference for America's children: Speech-language pathologists in public schools.* Eau Claire, WI: Thinking Publications.

National Association of State Directors of Special Education. (2006). *Response to intervention: Policy considerations and implementation.* Alexandria, VA: Author.

National Joint Committee on Learning Disabilities. (2005). *Responsiveness to intervention and learning disabilities* [Position Paper]. Bethesda, MD. **http://www.ldonline.org/njcld/index.html**

National Reading Panel. (2000). *Report of the national reading panel. Teaching children to read: An evidence-based assessment of the scientific research literature on reading and its implications for reading instruction.* (NIH Publication No. 00-4769). Washington DC: U.S. Government Printing Office.

Nelson, N. (1994). Curriculum-based language assessment and intervention across the grades. In G. Wallach & K. Butler (Eds.), *Language learning disabilities in school-age children and adolescents: Some principles and applications* (pp. 104-131). New York: Macmillan College Publishing.

Nicolosi, L., Harryman, E., & Kresheck, J. (1989). *Terminology of communication disorders of speech-language-hearing* (3rd ed.). Baltimore, MD: Williams & Wilkins.

Nunn, G.D., & McMahan, K.R. (2000). "Ideal" problem solving using a collaborative effort for special needs and at-risk students. *Education* (Winter). **http://findarticles.com/p/articles/mi_qa3673/is_200001/ai_n8885706**

Pearson, P.D., & Fielding. L. (1991). Comprehension instruction. In R. Barr, M.L. Kamil, P. Mosenthal, & P.D. Pearson (Eds.), *Handbook of reading research, Volume II,* (pp. 815-860). Mahwah, NJ: Lawrence Erlbaum Associates.

Peterson, K.M.H., & Shinn, M.R. (2002). Severe discrepancy models: Which best explains school identification practices for learning disabilities? *School Psychology Review, 31*(4), 459-477.

President's Commission on Excellence in Special Education. (2002). *A new era: Revitalizing special education for children and their families.* Washington DC: United States Department of Education/Author. **www.ed.gov/inits/commissionsboards/whspecialeducation/index.html**

Reschly, D.J., & Hosp, J.L. (2004). State SLD policies and practices. *Learning Disabilities Quarterly, 27,* 197-213.

Reschly, D.J., & Ysseldyke, J. (2002). Paradigm shift: The past is not the future. In A. Thomas & J. Grimes (Eds.). *Best practices in school psychology – IV* (4th ed.) (pp. 3-20). Bethesda, MD: National Association of School Psychologists. Roy, P., & Hord, S. (2003). *Moving NSDC's staff development standards into practice: Innovation configurations.* Oxford, OH: National Staff Development Council.

Roy, P., & Hord, S. (2003). *Moving NSDC's staff development standards into practice: Innovation configurations.* Oxford, OH: National Staff Development Council.

Salvia, J., & Ysseldyke, J.E. (1991). *Assessment* (5th ed.). Boston: Houghton Mifflin.

Shinn, M. (1989). *Curriculum-based measurement: Assessing special children.* New York: Guilford Press.

Sparks, D. (1993). *Thirteen tips for managing change.* North Central Regional Educational Laboratory. **http://www.ncrel.org/sdrs/areas/issues/educatrs/leadrshp/le5spark.htm**

Taps, J. (2006). *Articulation resource center model.* Unpublished manuscript, San Diego Unified School District.

Texas Essential Knowledge and Skills. **http://www.tea.state.tx.us/teks/**

Torgeson, J.K. (2000). Individual differences in response to early interventions in reading: The lingering problem of treatment resisters. *Learning Disabilities Research & Practice, 15*(1), 55-64.

Torgeson, J.K. (2002). Empirical and theoretical support for direct diagnosis of learning disabilities by assessment of intrinsic processing weaknesses. In R. Bradley, L. Danielson, & D. Hallahan (Eds.), *Identification of learning disabilities: Research to practice* (pp. 565-613). Mahwah, NJ: Lawrence Erlbaum Associates.

Torgeson, J.K., Alexander, A.W., Wagneer, R.K., Rashotte, C.A., Voeller, K.K.S., & Conway, T. (2001). Intensive remedial instruction for children with severe reading disabilities: Immediate and long-term outcomes from two instructional approaches. *Journal of Learning Disabilities, 34,* 33-58.

Turner, R. (2007). *Discipline for special education students: Discretionary ISS, DAEP & expulsions.* Dallas, TX: Author.

U.S. Department of Education. (1999). *21ˢᵗ annual report to Congress on the implementation of the Individuals with Disabilities Education Act (IDEA).* Washington DC: U.S. Government Printing Office.

U.S. Department of Education. (2002). *No Child Left Behind Act of 2001: Reauthorization of the Elementary and Secondary Education Act.* **www.ed.gov/nclb/landing.jhtml**

U.S. Department of Education. (2003). *25ᵗʰ annual report to Congress on the implementation of the Individuals with Disabilities Education Act (IDEA).* Washington DC: U.S. Government Printing Office.

Vaughn Gross Center for Preventing Reading Difficulties. (2005). *Preventing reading difficulties: A three-tiered intervention model.* Current research in press. **http://texasreading.org/3tier**

Vaughn, S., & Fuchs, L.S. (2003). Redefining learning disabilities as inadequate response to instruction: The promise and potential problems. *Learning Disabilities Research and Practice, 18,* 137-146.

Vaughn, S., & Wanzek, J. (2006). *Preventing reading difficulties: A three-tiered intervention model.* **http://www.nrcld.org/rti_practices/research/k3.html**

Vygotsky, L.S. (1978). *Mind in society* (M. Cole, V. John-Steiner, S. Scribner, & E. Soberman, Eds.). Cambridge, MA: Harvard University Press.

Walker, H.M., Horner, R.H., Sugai, G., Bullis, M., Sprague, J.R., Bricker, D., & Kaufman, M.J. (1996). Integrated approaches to preventing antisocial behavior patterns among school-age children and youth. *Journal of Emotional and Behavioral Disorders, 4,* 194-209.

Walton, M. (1986). *The Deming management method.* New York: Perigree Books.

Wiechmann, J., & Balfanz, D. (2007). *Artic lab: A bilingual response to intervention (RTI) program for articulation.* Greenville, SC: Super Duper Publications.

23-08-98765432